Best wishes

Freddie Ardili

BRIDGE IN THE LOOKING-GLASS

BRIDGE IN THE LOOKING-GLASS

Compare Your Play with the Masters
in 100 selected hands

Jeremy Flint and Freddie North

with a foreword by
OMAR SHARIF

CASSELL · LONDON

CASSELL & COMPANY LTD
35 Red Lion Square, London WC1
Sydney, Auckland
Toronto, Johannesburg

First published 1971

I.S.B.N. 0 304 93776 2 (cased)
I.S.B.N. 0 304 93777 0 (paperback)

Printed in Great Britain by
The Camelot Press Ltd, London and Southampton
F.671

FOREWORD

by Omar Sharif

When Jeremy Flint and Freddie North asked me to introduce *Bridge in the Looking-Glass* to its readers I accepted with enthusiasm. To the compulsive bridge-player there is no greater pleasure than playing difficult hands in good company, and the more he is in the hot seat the better. To read this book, as I expected, is to play a 100-hand session under these conditions: the opposition the best in the world, and at least one moment of crisis on every deal. My guess is that very few players would achieve a ten per cent record at the table.

However, this is better than the real thing: you have more time, and if you do go wrong you have the consolation of expert assistance in the post-mortem. I have learnt the hard way that the authors are highly qualified to give such assistance, for I have played against them both many times—against Jeremy Flint in international contests all over the world, especially the marathon match in London during 1970; and against Freddie North in friendly—or comparatively friendly—rubber games at the Hamilton Club, with nothing more serious than money at stake.

It remains for me only to wish the reader luck: while he is reading the book he will certainly need it. But when he returns to the table he will find that his luck has inexplicably changed for the better.

CONTENTS

DEFENCE

'Give me the cards and I'll play them as well as anyone.' You've said it often enough—now prove it. The hundred hands in this book come from all levels of the game, from World Championships to family rubber bridge, and many were first handled—or mishandled—by one of the world's leading experts. Now you are faced with the same problem—can you do better?

We have collected these hands one by one over several years, and they are not meant to be easy. In adopting the well-tried 'quizbook' formula—each problem on a right-hand page with solution and analysis on the following left-hand page—we have tried to combine entertainment and instruction: the book should be regarded as more than just a test of card-playing skill. And in most cases we have given the case-history of the hands, several of which show that the game at the top is not always as serious as might be supposed.

Hands like these do not occur all the time, of course, and it is perfectly possible to enjoy the game without mastering the advanced plays which are necessary to solve most of the problems in this book. But how much more satisfying to recognize one, to negotiate it successfully, and to land a contract which last week you would have written off with the time-honoured formula: 'Unlucky—everything was wrong.' It is the player who still gets home when everything is wrong who carries off the money or the master-points, and obtains the most pleasure from the game.

JEREMY FLINT *and* FREDDIE NORTH

DUMMY-PLAY

Pairs
North–South vulnerable
Dealer North

♠ 7 5 4 3
♡ —
♢ A 10 7 3
♣ A K Q J 7

```
        N
    W       E
        S
```

♠9 led

♠ K 8
♡ A Q 10 8
♢ Q J 5 4
♣ 10 8 5

Bidding:

SOUTH	WEST	NORTH	EAST
		1 ◇	Double
Redouble	Pass	2 ♣	2 ♠
3 NT	Pass	Pass	Double
Pass	Pass	Pass	

West leads the nine of spades against South's contract of three no trumps doubled. East wins with the ace and plays the queen of spades, West following with the two.

How should declarer plan the play?

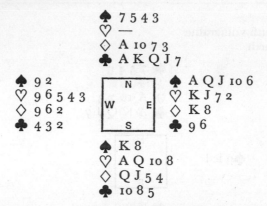

♠ 7 5 4 3
♡ —
♢ A 10 7 3
♣ A K Q J 7

♠ 9 2   ♠ A Q J 10 6
♡ 9 6 5 4 3   ♡ K J 7 2
♢ 9 6 2   ♢ K 8
♣ 4 3 2   ♣ 9 6

♠ K 8
♡ A Q 10 8
♢ Q J 5 4
♣ 10 8 5

It is clear that East must hold all the outstanding honour cards, thus there is no point in taking the diamond finesse. Declarer should play three rounds of clubs and exit with a spade. East can cash his winners but then must concede an extra trick in one of the red suits; or alternatively, though this would be an inferior line, South can cash ♡A at trick three and run the club suit. Unless East throws a diamond he will subsequently be thrown in with a spade to lead away from his ♢ K 8.

This hand occurred in the Mixed Pairs Championships at the Eastbourne Congress and helped the renowned partnership of Boris

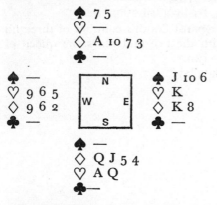

♠ 7 5
♡ —
♢ A 10 7 3
♣ —

♠ —   ♠ J 10 6
♡ 9 6 5   ♡ K
♢ 9 6 2   ♢ K 8
♣ —   ♣ —

♠ —
♢ Q J 5 4
♡ A Q
♣ —

Schapiro (West) and Rixi Markus (East) on the way to victory. The declarer made two errors—one venial and one fatal. Having failed to cash ♡A at trick three, he ran the entire club suit to arrive at the diagram position, North to play. Mrs Markus was thrown on lead at this point with a spade. However, the third spade squeezed declarer and Mrs Markus was in complete control. Schapiro retained his three diamonds and South ♡ A Q and ♢Q. Now Mrs Markus played ♢K and West took the setting trick with his ♢9. 'Just as well I had a bit in reserve,' quipped Boris.

Rubber bridge
North–South vulnerable
Dealer North

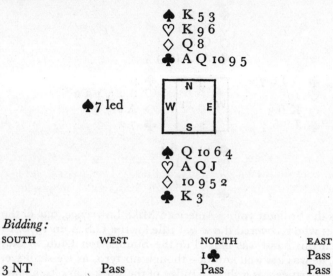

♠ K 5 3
♡ K 9 6
◇ Q 8
♣ A Q 10 9 5

♠ 7 led

♠ Q 10 6 4
♡ A Q J
◇ 10 9 5 2
♣ K 3

Bidding:

SOUTH	WEST	NORTH	EAST
		1♣	Pass
3 NT	Pass	Pass	Pass

'Handsome is as handsome does' might well describe the bidding.
West leads the seven of spades, East contribùting the nine.
  How should South plan the play?

The Bludgeon and the Rapier

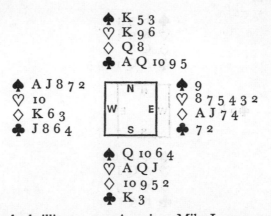

```
                ♠ K 5 3
                ♡ K 9 6
                ◇ Q 8
                ♣ A Q 10 9 5
  ♠ A J 8 7 2      N        ♠ 9
  ♡ 10                      ♡ 8 7 5 4 3 2
  ◇ K 6 3     W       E     ◇ A J 7 4
  ♣ J 8 6 4      S          ♣ 7 2
                ♠ Q 10 6 4
                ♡ A Q J
                ◇ 10 9 5 2
                ♣ K 3
```

South was the brilliant young American Mike Lawrence, one of the Dallas Aces who recovered the world title for the U.S.A. in 1970. In 1966, when this hand was played at the Summerton Club in San Francisco, he was less well known—though no tyro, as we shall see. Lawrence's partner was a shrewd judge of the stock markets, a good husband and a fine father. Having reasonably employed the bludgeon in the bidding Lawrence produced the rapier in the play. Winning the first trick with ♠10 he immediately returned a spade. West ducked, perforce, as otherwise declarer has nine tricks. Now came the second key play, a *diamond* from dummy. Three hearts, three clubs, two spades and the diamond Lawrence eventually established were enough tricks to fulfil the contract. Clearly if declarer had tried to establish the clubs the defence would have had five tricks: one spade, one club and three diamonds.

An elderly kibitzer could not resist a word of advice. 'Young man, when you play no trumps you should establish your long suit.' One of the authors could only force a rueful smile as he settled his losses on the rubber.

Teams
Game all
Dealer South

♠ Q 5
♡ J 10 6
♢ 9 7 5 2
♣ A Q 6 4

♠K led

N / W E / S

♠ A 3
♡ A Q 9 8 4
♢ K Q 6
♣ 9 3 2

Bidding:

SOUTH	WEST	NORTH	EAST
1♡	1♠	2♡	Pass
2♠	Pass	3♠	Pass
3 NT	Pass	Pass	Pass

Needing to find some points in a teams-of-four match, South continued with a dubious two spades over his partner's limit raise to two hearts. Even though North had a little to spare it was still essential to play the contract from the right hand. That this had been achieved was readily apparent when West led the king of spades.

How should declarer plan the play?

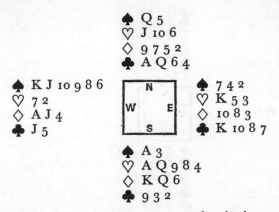

Declarer, who has won every cup worth winning, made an un-characteristic play when, on winning with ♠A, he led a club to dummy's ♣Q. East won and knocked out the second spade guard, leaving South with no more than eight tricks (five hearts, two spades and one club), for there was now no time to establish a diamond.

South should have appreciated that there would be virtually no chance unless East held ♡K. Thus a club to ♣A at trick two would have given him time to enjoy a diamond trick after picking up ♡K. The position of ♣K was immaterial, and dummy's ♣Q only acted as a tender trap!

Rubber bridge
North–South vulnerable
Dealer West

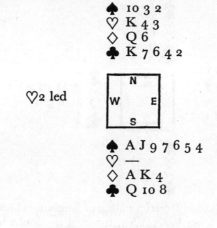

♠ 10 3 2
♡ K 4 3
◇ Q 6
♣ K 7 6 4 2

♡2 led

♠ A J 9 7 6 5 4
♡ —
◇ A K 4
♣ Q 10 8

Bidding:

SOUTH	WEST	NORTH	EAST
	Pass	Pass	4♡
4♠	Double	Pass	Pass
Pass			

West leads the two of hearts against South's contract of four spades doubled.

How should South plan the play?

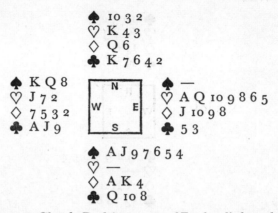

```
              ♠ 10 3 2
              ♡ K 4 3
              ◇ Q 6
              ♣ K 7 6 4 2
♠ K Q 8                         ♠ —
♡ J 7 2          N              ♡ A Q 10 9 8 6 5
◇ 7 5 3 2    W       E          ◇ J 10 9 8
♣ A J 9          S              ♣ 5 3
              ♠ A J 9 7 6 5 4
              ♡ —
              ◇ A K 4
              ♣ Q 10 8
```

This hand features Claude Rodrigue, one of England's best dummy-players. After a pass from West, East, fortified no doubt by favourable vulnerability conditions, decided on bold tactics. Rodrigue (South) was not to be shut out; nor was West, who must have been supremely confident.

Sensing that two trump tricks would have to be lost, Claude's main concern was to avoid losing more than one club trick. Thus he played for an unusual form of elimination. Ruffing the heart in hand he entered dummy with ◇Q and ruffed a second heart. ◇ A K followed on which dummy's last heart was thrown. Now a small spade towards ♠10 left West with the choice of conceding a ruff and discard, opening up the club suit or jettisoning his second trump trick.

Rubber bridge
North–South vulnerable
Dealer East

♠ K 8 6 4 2
♡ 4 3
◇ K 4 3
♣ A 9 5

♡K led

```
      N
  W       E
      S
```

♠ A Q J 10 9
♡ A 2
◇ A 5 2
♣ 7 6 4

Bidding:

SOUTH	WEST	NORTH	EAST
			Pass
1♠	4♡	4♠	Pass
Pass	Pass		

West leads the king of hearts, which East ruffs! A nasty jolt—how do
you recover? Faced with the prospect of four apparently inevitable
losers, declarer must conceive a plan which is capable of success.

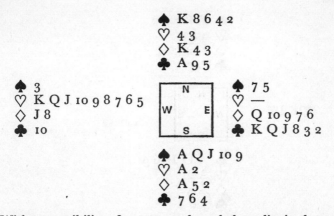

With no possibility of a squeeze, the only hope lies in the rare double ruff and discard. West, in addition to his nine hearts, will have to hold precisely one club and two diamonds. At trick one declarer must jettison his ♡A. He wins the club return and draws the adverse trumps. After cashing ◇ A K he exits with a heart. West, who has only hearts left, is forced to give declarer the opportunity of discarding a diamond from dummy while he disposes of a club from his own hand. The next heart is ruffed in dummy while declarer's last club goes away.

Rubber bridge
Game all
Dealer South

♠ A K 7
♡ 7 6 2
◇ A K 10 4
♣ 6 3 2

♠Q led

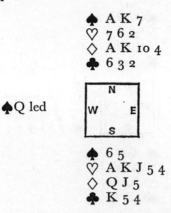

♠ 6 5
♡ A K J 5 4
◇ Q J 5
♣ K 5 4

South plays in four hearts, the opponents having passed throughout. The queen of spades is led; dummy wins and East plays low. The two of hearts is played from dummy, East following with the three.

How should declarer plan the play?

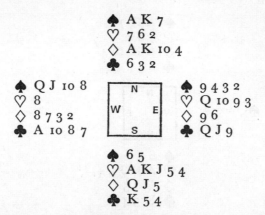

```
                        ♠ A K 7
                        ♡ 7 6 2
                        ◇ A K 10 4
                        ♣ 6 3 2
        ♠ Q J 10 8                        ♠ 9 4 3 2
        ♡ 8              N               ♡ Q 10 9 3
        ◇ 8 7 3 2     W     E           ◇ 9 6
        ♣ A 10 8 7       S               ♣ Q J 9
                        ♠ 6 5
                        ♡ A K J 5 4
                        ◇ Q J 5
                        ♣ K 5 4
```

Declarer must cover East's ♡3 with ♡4! No matter that it loses to ♡8. When declarer regains the lead a top heart reveals the trump position, and the remainder of East's trumps can be picked up without loss. The crucial factor is that East is denied the lead; thus he can never attack South's unprotected ♣K—until South has drawn trumps and taken one discard.

No doubt West was delighted to win a trick with ♡8, even though his pleasure was short-lived.

Teams
East–West vulnerable
Dealer West

♠ 6 5 4 3
♥ Q 4 2
♦ A K 8
♣ 7 5 4

♥K led

```
      N
   W     E
      S
```

♠ A K Q J 9 8
♥ —
♦ 6 3 2
♣ A K 6 2

After West has opened with a pre-emptive bid of three hearts, South becomes the declarer in six spades. The king of hearts is led and ruffed by South. The ace and king of spades follow, East throwing a small heart on the second round.

How should declarer continue?

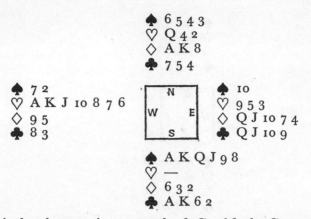

```
              ♠ 6 5 4 3
              ♡ Q 4 2
              ◇ A K 8
              ♣ 7 5 4

♠ 7 2              N              ♠ 10
♡ A K J 10 8 7 6        W    E    ♡ 9 5 3
◇ 9 5                   S         ◇ Q J 10 7 4
♣ 8 3                            ♣ Q J 10 9

              ♠ A K Q J 9 8
              ♡ —
              ◇ 6 3 2
              ♣ A K 6 2
```

This hand arose in a round of Crockfords Cup, the teams' championship of England. Both declarers arrived in 6♠ after similar bidding sequences. The first three tricks were the same in both rooms. Then the first declarer cashed ♣A, ◇A and ♣K. Finally he resigned himself to a 3–3 club break when he played a third club. Minus 50 was his just reward.

The second declarer, M. Harrison-Gray, swiftly discarded the notion of an even club break. West was likely to have seven hearts; thus it seemed that East had nine cards in the minors. If he had three clubs then he must hold six diamonds, and no doubt would have discarded one on the second spade. By no means conclusive, but extremely probable. Accordingly Harrison-Gray played a diamond to ◇A, ruffed a low heart, cashed his two top clubs and played a diamond to ◇K. Now ♡Q, on which he discarded his last diamond, forced West to concede a ruff and discard, enabling declarer to make the remainder of the tricks on a cross-ruff.

Rubber bridge
North–South game +60
Dealer West

```
                         ♠ K J 10 5
                         ♡ 6 4 2
                         ◇ 7 5 3
                         ♣ J 4 2

                        ┌─────────┐
                        │    N    │
       ♣Q led           │ W     E │
                        │    S    │
                        └─────────┘

                         ♠ A Q 7
                         ♡ K J 7 5
                         ◇ A K 10 8 4
                         ♣ 6
```

Bidding:

SOUTH	WEST	NORTH	EAST
	Pass	Pass	1♣
Double	Pass	1♠	2♣
2◇	3♣	3◇	4♣
4◇	Double	Pass	Pass
Pass			

West leads the queen of clubs against South's contract of four diamonds doubled. When the queen wins he continues with a second club, ruffed by South. The ace of diamonds, on which East plays the jack, is followed by a low spade to dummy's ten. South continues with a heart from dummy, East following with the three.

How should declarer plan the play from this point?

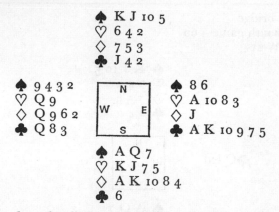

♠ K J 10 5
♡ 6 4 2
◇ 7 5 3
♣ J 4 2

♠ 9 4 3 2   ♠ 8 6
♡ Q 9   ♡ A 10 8 3
◇ Q 9 6 2   ◇ J
♣ Q 8 3   ♣ A K 10 9 7 5

♠ A Q 7
♡ K J 7 5
◇ A K 10 8 4
♣ 6

South was that dazzling personality and idol of the screen, Egyptian international Omar Sharif. Reasoning that ♡A must be with East and that West must surely have started with ◇ Q 9 6 2, he directed his mind to the distribution of the major suits and the endgame. If West held four spades it was immaterial who held ♡Q. All would be well if West held a third club. Sharif appreciated that even if East held ♡ A Q x it could hardly gain to put in ♡J, since dummy would be short of an entry to play hearts a second time *and* lead a third round of clubs for the all-important trump reduction play.

Having followed Sharif's thoughts we return to the action. At trick five he went in with ♡K, and when this held he played off all the spades, discarding a heart from hand. Sharif had only lost one trick. He ruffed dummy's club, and this was the position with South to play:

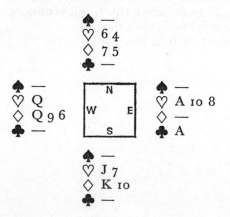

♠ —
♡ 6 4
◇ 7 5
♣ —

♠ —   ♠ —
♡ Q   ♡ A 10 8
◇ Q 9 6   ◇ —
♣ —   ♣ A

♠ —
♡ J 7
◇ K 10
♣ —

When declarer led a heart East overtook his partner's ♡Q and played another heart, but this did not save West from conceding the last two tricks to Omar Sharif's diamond tenace.

Teams
East–West vulnerable
Dealer North

```
                    ♠ 5
                    ♡ K Q 10 6
                    ◇ A Q 5
                    ♣ K Q 9 5 3

                    ┌─────────┐
                    │    N    │
    ♠ 4 led         │ W     E │
                    │    S    │
                    └─────────┘

                    ♠ A Q 10
                    ♡ J 9 7
                    ◇ K 7 4 2
                    ♣ J 6 4
```

Bidding:

SOUTH	WEST	NORTH	EAST
		1 ♣	Pass
1 ◇	Pass	1 ♡	Pass
2 NT	Pass	3 ◇	Pass
3 NT	Pass	Pass	Pass

West leads the four of spades against South's contract of three no trumps, East playing the jack.

How should South plan the play?

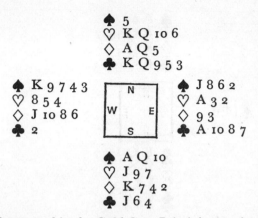

♠ 5
♡ K Q 10 6
◇ A Q 5
♣ K Q 9 5 3

♠ K 9 7 4 3
♡ 8 5 4
◇ J 10 8 6
♣ 2

♠ J 8 6 2
♡ A 3 2
◇ 9 3
♣ A 10 8 7

♠ A Q 10
♡ J 9 7
◇ K 7 4 2
♣ J 6 4

This hand occurred in the Gold Cup, Britain's premier event. South was the British international Jim Sharples. In the other room, where the contract was also 3NT, at trick two declarer played a low club to dummy's ♣K, which lost to ♣A. East returned a spade and now there was no way of making nine tricks before the defence took five.

The correct play, as Jim Sharples demonstrated, was to lead a diamond to dummy at trick two and follow with a small club towards ♣J. East had no option but to duck, and now declarer turned his attention to hearts. Thus he made two spades, three hearts, three diamonds and one club. This line succeeds against any distribution of the opposing cards, except where East has all five clubs and takes his ♣A on the first round.

Teams
Game all
Dealer East

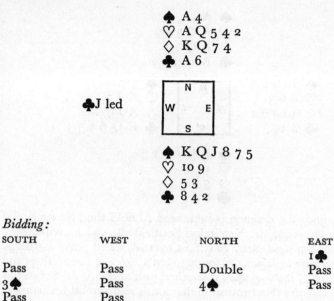

♠ A 4
♡ A Q 5 4 2
♢ K Q 7 4
♣ A 6

♣ J led

N
W   E
S

♠ K Q J 8 7 5
♡ 10 9
♢ 5 3
♣ 8 4 2

Bidding:

SOUTH	WEST	NORTH	EAST
			1 ♣
Pass	Pass	Double	Pass
3 ♠	Pass	4 ♠	Pass
Pass	Pass		

Against South's contract of four spades West leads the jack of clubs.
How should declarer plan the play?

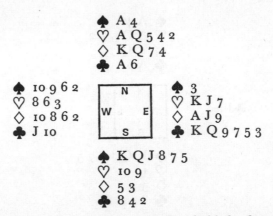

♠ A 4
♡ A Q 5 4 2
◇ K Q 7 4
♣ A 6

♠ 10 9 6 2   ♠ 3
♡ 8 6 3   ♡ K J 7
◇ 10 8 6 2   ◇ A J 9
♣ J 10   ♣ K Q 9 7 5 3

♠ K Q J 8 7 5
♡ 10 9
◇ 5 3
♣ 8 4 2

Strangely, once the defence is permitted to hold the first trick, the contract is impregnable. Yet unless South ducks ♣J he will surely be defeated. Suppose, first, that East overtakes and plays a trump. Dummy wins and plays ◇K forcing East's ◇A—if East refuses the first round, ◇Q follows. ♣A is knocked out, and now all South has to do is to ruff the third round of diamonds and run all his trumps, eventually throwing East in with a club to concede the last two heart tricks.

If clubs are continued by the defence at trick two, ◇K again opens up the communications. If East plays anything but a trump, having won ◇A, declarer can pick up his club ruff without losing a trump trick to West.

When this hand was dealt in a county match, three declarers were defeated in 4♠ (once it was doubled and redoubled). In each case ♣J was led and won in dummy. The ♣6 followed, East winning and switching to a trump. There was now no way in which declarer could avoid losing four tricks.

Pairs
Love all
Dealer South

```
                      ♠ J 8 5 2
                      ♡ A 6
                      ◇ Q J 9 8 5
                      ♣ K 8

                    ┌─────────┐
                    │    N    │
       ♣ J led      │ W     E │
                    │    S    │
                    └─────────┘

                      ♠ A Q 6
                      ♡ Q 5 3
                      ◇ A K 10 4
                      ♣ A 7 2
```

West leads the jack of clubs against South's ambitious contract of six diamonds. Dummy wins, and the trumps are cleared in two rounds.

How should declarer continue?

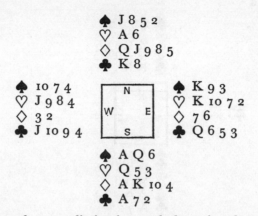

South must plan an elimination and throw-in play, unless East turns up with ♠K x or ♠K alone. The clubs are eliminated and the spade finesse is followed by ♠A and a small spade. East must now lead from his ♡K or concede a ruff and discard.

Rubber bridge
North–South vulnerable
Dealer West

```
                    ♠ K J 8 4
                    ♡ K Q
                    ◇ A K Q 6 3
                    ♣ Q 6

                    ┌─────────┐
                    │    N    │
    ♣9 led          │ W     E │
                    │    S    │
                    └─────────┘

                    ♠ A 10 6
                    ♡ A 9 8 7 6 2
                    ◇ J 5 4
                    ♣ 5
```

Bidding:

SOUTH	WEST	NORTH	EAST
	Pass	2 NT	Pass
3♡	Pass	4♡	Pass
4♠	Pass	5◇	Pass
6♡	Pass	Pass	Pass

The bidding might not please everyone but the final contract is reasonable. West leads the nine of clubs, won by East's ace. The jack of clubs is continued and ruffed by South. On dummy's top hearts West follows with the jack and then discards a club on the next round. South plays a diamond to his jack and a second diamond, on which West shows out.

How should South continue?

27

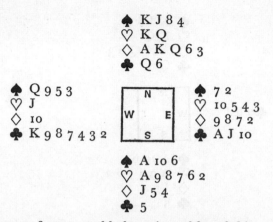

South was a former world champion, although his performance on this hand would never have given any indication of the fact! Having ruffed the second club he tabled his cards and said, 'Well, has anyone got four hearts?' East claimed this privilege, so there was nothing for it but to concede one down.

After the trump distribution has been discovered, declarer should play four rounds of diamonds, ruffing the fourth round in hand. Then he cashes ♠A and leads a spade to dummy's ♠J. When this card holds the rest is plain sailing. Dummy plays ♢Q, and East can either surrender immediately or prolong the agony for one more round.

Rubber bridge
North–South vulnerable
Dealer East

♠ 10 7 6 4
♡ A Q
♢ J 8 3
♣ 9 7 4 3

♡4 led

```
    N
W       E
    S
```

♠ A K
♡ 9 7 5 3
♢ A Q 10 9 5
♣ A K

Bidding:

SOUTH	WEST	NORTH	EAST
			Pass
1 ♢	Pass	1 ♠	Pass
3 NT	Pass	Pass	Pass

West leads the four of hearts against South's contract of three no trumps.

How should South plan the play?

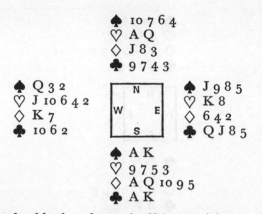

```
                    ♠ 10 7 6 4
                    ♡ A Q
                    ◇ J 8 3
                    ♣ 9 7 4 3
♠ Q 3 2                            ♠ J 9 8 5
♡ J 10 6 4 2          N            ♡ K 8
◇ K 7           W         E        ◇ 6 4 2
♣ 10 6 2             S             ♣ Q J 8 5
                    ♠ A K
                    ♡ 9 7 5 3
                    ◇ A Q 10 9 5
                    ♣ A K
```

Declarer should play dummy's ♡A at trick one, resisting any temptation to finesse. Applying the rule of eleven to the opening lead, it appears that East has two cards higher than ♡4. Unless West has played specifically from ♡ K J 10 *and* holds ◇K the contract is assured, since the play of ♡A will effectively block the suit. It is also worth noting that at favourable vulnerability West might have come in with 1♡ over 1◇ if he had ♡ K J 10 and ◇K.

Declarer has to take one other minor precaution. When he plays the diamond suit from dummy he must play ◇8 first, and then ◇J (or ◇J unblocking ◇9 or ◇10 from his own hand) so as to cater for East holding ◇ K x x x (x).

VIVE LA DIFFÉRENCE!

Teams
North–South vulnerable
Dealer South

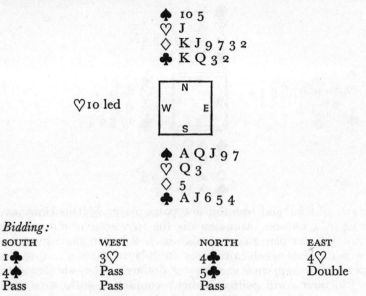

♠ 10 5
♡ J
◇ K J 9 7 3 2
♣ K Q 3 2

♡ 10 led

♠ A Q J 9 7
♡ Q 3
◇ 5
♣ A J 6 5 4

Bidding:

SOUTH	WEST	NORTH	EAST
1♣	3♡	4♣	4♡
4♠	Pass	5♣	Double
Pass	Pass	Pass	

West leads the ten of hearts against South's contract of five clubs doubled. East wins with the king and switches to the ten of clubs, West discarding a small heart.

How should South continue?

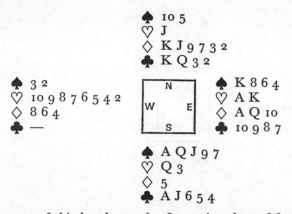

The star of this hand was the fine pairs player Martin Hoffman. Playing in a multiple team event in the 1970 season he made one slightly different play to his rivals who had bid to game in clubs. He won the club switch in dummy and played ♠10 . . . but wait; let us see what happened to the other declarers. They also led ♠10 at trick three, and when it held continued with a second spade finesse. ♠A revealed the 4–2 break, and a spade was ruffed in dummy. Dummy now exited with a diamond, won by East, who played a second round of trumps. Declarer had to win in dummy to avoid establishing a high trump for East. But now the problem of getting to hand, ruffing a heart in dummy and returning to hand to draw the trumps and enjoy the thirteenth spade proved insurmountable. Each declarer had to admit defeat.

Martin Hoffman's solution? He overtook ♠10 with ♠J, ruffed ♡Q and took a second spade finesse. Now, after a spade ruff and top club from dummy, he was able to exit from dummy with a diamond and without waiting for East's next card he claimed the remainder of the tricks.

The difference between the two lines of play was so small—yet so vital. As the French would say, *Vive la différence!*

Rubber bridge
North–South vulnerable
Dealer East

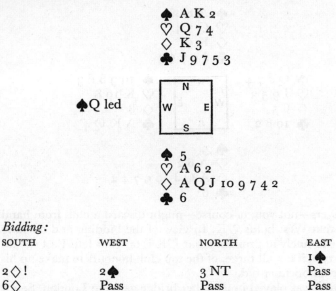

♠ A K 2
♡ Q 7 4
◇ K 3
♣ J 9 7 5 3

♠Q led

♠ 5
♡ A 6 2
◇ A Q J 10 9 7 4 2
♣ 6

Bidding:

SOUTH	WEST	NORTH	EAST
			1♠
2◇!	2♠	3 NT	Pass
6◇	Pass	Pass	Pass

West leads the queen of spades against South's contract of six diamonds. How should declarer plan the play?

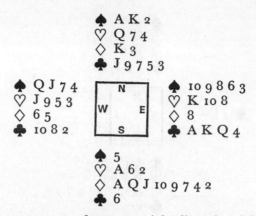

Some players—not you, of course—might discard a club from hand and *hope* that West holds ♡K. In view of the bidding and opening lead it is extremely improbable that ♡K is on your left. East should also hold two, if not all three, of the top club honours to make up his values for an opening bid.

This hand was played in a rubber bridge game in London. South was Mrs Gertie Gottesmann, a former Belgian international. Deciding to play the auction by ear, she contracted for the small slam when partner showed good values. Reading the position correctly she won the first trick with ♠A, cashed a second top spade and discarded a heart from her hand. Now she ran all the diamonds reducing everyone to three cards. East was then thrown in with the best club and forced to concede the last two tricks. Once West showed ♠ Q J it was a fair inference to assume that East had ♡K and ♣A K Q to justify his opening bid.

Teams
North–South vulnerable
Dealer South

                    ♠ 3
                    ♡ Q 10 3 2
                    ◇ K J 4 3
                    ♣ J 10 7 6

♣Q led

                    ♠ A Q 9 8 7
                    ♡ K J 7 6
                    ◇ —
                    ♣ A 8 5 3

Bidding:

SOUTH	WEST	NORTH	EAST
1♠	2◇	Pass	Pass
Double	Pass	3◇	Pass
3♡	Pass	4♡	Pass
Pass	Pass		

West leads the queen of clubs against South's contract of four hearts. Declarer wins and leads the six of hearts, West playing the eight, dummy the ten and East the ace. East cashes the king of clubs, West playing the two, and then leads a third club, West ruffing with the nine of hearts. After deep thought West plays the ace of diamonds, East contributing the two.

How should declarer plan the play?

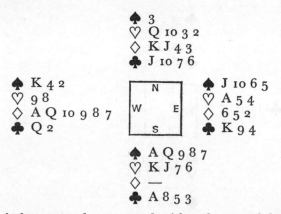

```
                    ♠ 3
                    ♡ Q 10 3 2
                    ◇ K J 4 3
                    ♣ J 10 7 6
♠ K 4 2          ┌──────────┐        ♠ J 10 6 5
♡ 9 8            │    N     │        ♡ A 5 4
◇ A Q 10 9 8 7   │ W     E  │        ◇ 6 5 2
♣ Q 2            │    S     │        ♣ K 9 4
                 └──────────┘
                    ♠ A Q 9 8 7
                    ♡ K J 7 6
                    ◇ —
                    ♣ A 8 5 3
```

West is known to have started with only two clubs, and almost certainly two hearts. His diamond suit is likely to be a six-carder since East would hardly have remained silent throughout the auction with four diamonds, ♡A and ♣K. Therefore West holds three spades to the king! Having assessed the distribution South can now proceed on double-dummy lines. He ruffs the diamond with ♡7, cashes ♠A and ruffs a spade. ◇K comes next, on which South makes the key play of discarding his last club. Now dummy's master club is played and East is confronted with a dilemma. If he fails to trump declarer gets home on a cross-ruff, while if he kills the club South overruffs and can now establish his spades.

This hand occurred in the final of the 1968–9 Hubert Phillips Bowl, the English Bridge Union's mixed teams-of-four championship. In one room the declarer was the young English star Ian Panto, who played the hand as described. In the other room the first round of bidding was the same, but then when South reopened with a double everyone passed. Seven tricks were made, so North–South netted a meagre 100 points.

Teams
Game all
Dealer South

```
           ♠ A 3 2
           ♡ Q 6 4
           ♦ A Q J 10 8
           ♣ 10 5

                ┌─────────┐
                │    N    │
♠J led          │ W     E │
                │    S    │
                └─────────┘

           ♠ K Q
           ♡ J 10 8 3
           ♦ 9 5 3
           ♣ A J 8 4
```

Bidding:

SOUTH	WEST	NORTH	EAST
Pass	Pass	1 ♦	Pass
2 NT	Pass	3 NT	Pass
Pass	Pass		

West leads the jack of spades against South's contract of three no trumps, reached without opposition bidding.

How should declarer plan the play?

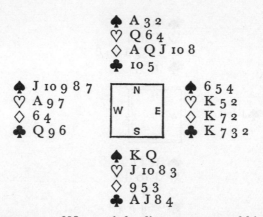

♠ A 3 2
♡ Q 6 4
◇ A Q J 10 8
♣ 10 5

♠ J 10 9 8 7   ♠ 6 5 4
♡ A 9 7   ♡ K 5 2
◇ 6 4   ◇ K 7 2
♣ Q 9 6   ♣ K 7 3 2

♠ K Q
♡ J 10 8 3
◇ 9 5 3
♣ A J 8 4

Louis Ström, one of Norway's leading stars, earned his team a game swing when this hand occurred in the 1964 Scandinavian Championships. His counterpart in the other room, also in 3 NT, finessed a diamond at trick two. East continued with a second spade and when South now turned his attention to hearts it was too late to prevent East clearing the spades. Subsequently West regained the lead and cashed his spade winners to set the contract by one trick.

Ström, readily appreciating the dangers of playing a diamond too early, led a small heart to ♡Q at trick two. East won and persevered with the spades (nothing else is better). Now ♡J forced West's ♡A, and Ström was able to return to his own hand and take the diamond finesse, secure in the knowledge that his contract could not fail as long as West had started with at least four spades.

Rubber bridge
Game all
Dealer East

```
                    ♠ K J 2
                    ♡ A Q
                    ◇ 9 8 7 5 3
                    ♣ 10 8 3
```

♣9 led

```
        N
    W       E
        S
```

```
                    ♠ A Q 10 9 8 7
                    ♡ 10 7
                    ◇ A Q
                    ♣ 6 5 2
```

Bidding:

SOUTH	WEST	NORTH	EAST
			1 ♣
1 ♠	Pass	2 ♣	Pass
Pass	2 NT	3 ♠	Pass
Pass	Pass		

When North–South subsided in two spades West made a valiant effort to secure the contract in one of the remaining suits, but North was not to be denied.

West leads the nine of clubs and East cashes the king, queen and jack, obviously still holding the ace. He now switches to the four of diamonds.

How should declarer plan the play?

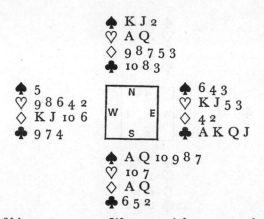

♠ K J 2
♡ A Q
♢ 9 8 7 5 3
♣ 10 8 3

♠ 5
♡ 9 8 6 4 2
♢ K J 10 6
♣ 9 7 4

♠ 6 4 3
♡ K J 5 3
♢ 4 2
♣ A K Q J

♠ A Q 10 9 8 7
♡ 10 7
♢ A Q
♣ 6 5 2

In spite of his meagre assets West was right to enter the auction or 4♡ by East–West cannot be defeated. As for South's problem in 3♠, he must resist the temptation of the diamond finesse. He should win trick four with ♢A, cash ♠A and exit with ♢Q. West wins and switches to a heart, but ♡A is played from dummy and a third round of diamonds is ruffed. With two spade entries left in dummy declarer can establish, and then enjoy, the last diamond for his ninth trick.

When this hand was played at the table South could not resist the lure of the diamond finesse. He still had the chance of the 3–3 break, but when that failed as well he complained bitterly about his bad luck. It is amusing to observe that he would almost certainly have made his contract if he had held a small diamond instead of ♢Q.

Pairs
Love all
Dealer South

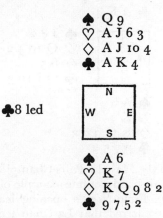

♠ Q 9
♡ A J 6 3
♢ A J 10 4
♣ A K 4

♣8 led

♠ A 6
♡ K 7
♢ K Q 9 8 2
♣ 9 7 5 2

Without opposition bidding South arrives in six diamonds. West leads the eight of clubs, East playing the queen on dummy's ace.

How should declarer plan the play (assuming the trumps are divided 2–2)?

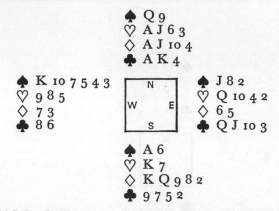

In 1966 John Collings won the Masters' Pairs Championship playing with Jonathan Cansino. This hand is a fine example of the dexterity of his sparkling card-play. From West's opening lead and East's play at trick one Collings inferred that East had length in clubs. Thus after two rounds of trumps, ♡K, ♡A and a heart ruff—♡Q might have come down—he played a second club to dummy, East contributing ♣3. Now a fourth heart was ruffed to reach this position:

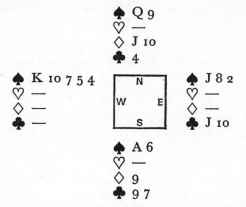

Reading the cards correctly, John Collings played ♠A and a small spade, forcing West to concede a ruff and discard for his twelfth trick. Had Collings decided that East held ♠K he could have attempted a squeeze throw-in in the black suits. As West was marked with length in spades Collings's selection of endplay was dictated by the odds.

Pairs
Love all
Dealer North

♠ A K J 6 5 2
♡ 8 6
♢ K 10 7 4
♣ 9

```
        N
    W       E
        S
```

♡3 led

♠ 10 4
♡ —
♢ Q J 5 3 2
♣ K Q J 10 6 4

Bidding:

SOUTH	WEST	NORTH	EAST
		1♠	2♡
3♣	3♡	Pass	4♡
5♣	Pass	Pass	Double
Pass	Pass	Pass	

West leads the three of hearts against South's contract of five clubs doubled. It is obvious that five diamonds would have been superior, but it is too late to change the bidding.

How should South plan the play?

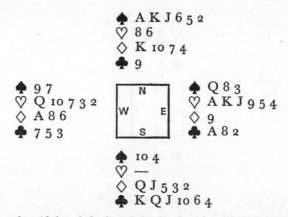

♠ A K J 6 5 2
♡ 8 6
◇ K 10 7 4
♣ 9

♠ 9 7
♡ Q 10 7 3 2
◇ A 8 6
♣ 7 5 3

♠ Q 8 3
♡ A K J 9 5 4
◇ 9
♣ A 8 2

♠ 10 4
♡ —
◇ Q J 5 3 2
♣ K Q J 10 6 4

It is clear that if the clubs break badly South will amost certainly be defeated, since he will not be able to survive the repeated force in hearts. Thus the main consideration is how to succeed if the trumps break 3–3. Then the only danger appears to be a diamond ruff. As an attempt to avert this South should lead ◇J at trick two. If he is allowed to hold the trick he must switch to ♣K.

This hand was played in the Mixed Pairs Championship at the 1970 Stockholm World Olympics. South was Mrs Fritzi Gordon, whose name is renowned in international bridge, and although she was by no means alone in playing in 5♣ doubled she was the only declarer to succeed. Visualizing the danger of the diamond ruff, she did her best to lessen the risk by playing ◇J at trick two. West ducked, as players will, and that was the last chance the defence had to obtain a plus score.

Teams
Game all
Dealer South

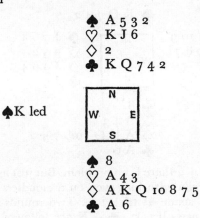

♠ A 5 3 2
♡ K J 6
◇ 2
♣ K Q 7 4 2

♠K led

♠ 8
♡ A 4 3
◇ A K Q 10 8 7 5
♣ A 6

After a well-judged auction, South arrives in seven diamonds, and West leads the king of spades.

Which card should declarer play from dummy at trick two?

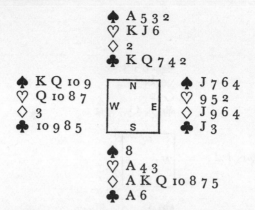

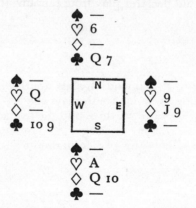

If the diamonds are 3–2 there is no problem. But just as the prudent man takes his umbrella with him even on a cloudless day, the declarer should ruff a spade at trick two. Two rounds of diamonds follow and the bad news breaks. ♣ A K are followed by a second spade ruff. Now a heart to dummy's ♡J, a third spade ruff and a heart to dummy's ♡K leaves this position:

♣Q is played from dummy and East can resign. When this hand occurred in a duplicate match in Istanbul in 1965 the declarer was Halit Bigat, one of Turkey's leading players. Not unnaturally Bigat's team-mates were lavish in their praise, as this hand made the difference between victory and defeat.

Teams
North–South vulnerable
Dealer East

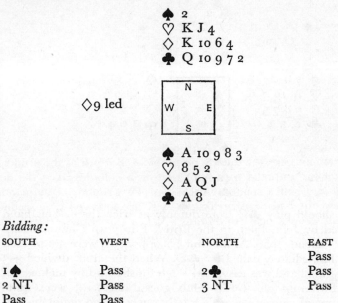

♠ 2
♡ K J 4
◇ K 10 6 4
♣ Q 10 9 7 2

◇9 led

♠ A 10 9 8 3
♡ 8 5 2
◇ A Q J
♣ A 8

Bidding:

SOUTH	WEST	NORTH	EAST
			Pass
1♠	Pass	2♣	Pass
2 NT	Pass	3 NT	Pass
Pass	Pass		

West leads the nine of diamonds against South's contract of three
no trumps. Winning in hand, South plays the ace and the eight of
clubs, West following with the three and the five and East with the
four.

Which card should declarer play from dummy, and why?

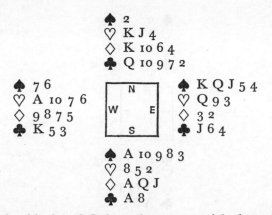

```
                    ♠ 2
                    ♡ K J 4
                    ◇ K 10 6 4
                    ♣ Q 10 9 7 2
  ♠ 7 6              ┌─────────┐        ♠ K Q J 5 4
  ♡ A 10 7 6        │    N    │        ♡ Q 9 3
  ◇ 9 8 7 5         │ W     E │        ◇ 3 2
  ♣ K 5 3           │    S    │        ♣ J 6 4
                    └─────────┘
                    ♠ A 10 9 8 3
                    ♡ 8 5 2
                    ◇ A Q J
                    ♣ A 8
```

Declarer should play ♣Q from dummy at trick three. This hand was played by John Pugh in the British European Championship Trials for Ostend, 1966. At the time his opponents were not pleased when he immediately called for ♣Q. When the clubs divided 3–3 the rest of the hand was easy, and Pugh finished up by making ten tricks. Mutterings of, 'Lucky club guess,' etcetera, were quite audible. But of course it wasn't a *lucky* guess, as no doubt his opponents would have been the first to acknowledge had they pondered on the problem a little longer. Pugh simply played with the odds. If he had played dummy's ♣9 and found East with ♣ K x he would still have had to lose two tricks in the suit. On the other hand, the play of ♣Q restricts the loss to one trick, not only when East holds ♣ J x x but also when he holds ♣ J x.

Rubber bridge
Love all, North–South +90
Dealer North

```
              ♠ K 7 4 2
              ♡ J 9 6
              ◇ A 8
              ♣ K Q 9 6

                 ┌─────────┐
                 │    N    │
  ♡A led         │ W     E │
                 │    S    │
                 └─────────┘

              ♠ A 8 5
              ♡ K Q 10 4
              ◇ K Q 10 9 5
              ♣ A
```

Bidding:

SOUTH	WEST	NORTH	EAST
		1 NT	Pass
2♣	Pass	2♠	Pass
6◇	Pass	Pass	Pass

Playing a 12–14 point no trump, South attempts to discover a heart
fit, but when this fails to materialize he settles for six diamonds.
West, a good player, leads the ace of hearts and, despite his partner's
two, continues the suit.

How should South plan the play?

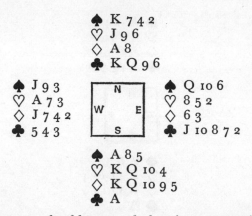

♠ K 7 4 2
♡ J 9 6
◇ A 8
♣ K Q 9 6

♠ J 9 3
♡ A 7 3
◇ J 7 4 2
♣ 5 4 3

♠ Q 10 6
♡ 8 5 2
◇ 6 3
♣ J 10 8 7 2

♠ A 8 5
♡ K Q 10 4
◇ K Q 10 9 5
♣ A

West's manœuvres should arouse declarer's grave suspicions. Why the rush to cash ♡A? This trick could hardly disappear—bearing in mind that North opened 1 NT and South gave a clear indication of holding four hearts. It is a reasonable hypothesis that West expects to make a trump trick. The evidence may appear slim, but the declarer, Boris Schapiro, has never lacked faith in his own analysis. He played a low diamond towards dummy and, despite West's crafty ◇7, put in the ◇8 to land his contract.

To his credit, West was the first to admit that his defence was too naïve to succeed against a player of Schapiro's calibre.

Pairs
Game all
Dealer South

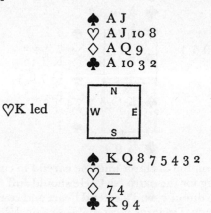

♠ A J
♥ A J 10 8
♦ A Q 9
♣ A 10 3 2

♥K led

♠ K Q 8 7 5 4 3 2
♥ —
♦ 7 4
♣ K 9 4

West leads the king of hearts against South's contract of seven spades.
    How should declarer plan the play (West has two spades and East one)?

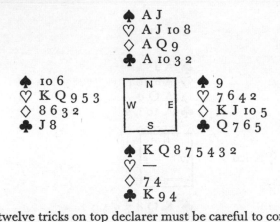

```
                    ♠ A J
                    ♡ A J 10 8
                    ◇ A Q 9
                    ♣ A 10 3 2
     ♠ 10 6                        ♠ 9
     ♡ K Q 9 5 3    ┌─────────┐    ♡ 7 6 4 2
     ◇ 8 6 3 2      │ N       │    ◇ K J 10 5
     ♣ J 8          │ W     E │    ♣ Q 7 6 5
                    │       S │
                    └─────────┘
                    ♠ K Q 8 7 5 4 3 2
                    ♡ —
                    ◇ 7 4
                    ♣ K 9 4
```

With twelve tricks on top declarer must be careful to combine all his chances when trying for the extra trick. He should ruff the first heart and lead a spade to dummy, ruff a second heart and re-enter dummy with the second spade. Declarer must make a critical decision at this point. Is it better to discard a club on ♡A and attempt to establish the long club by a ruff, or to discard a diamond, keeping the clubs intact for the end game?

The chance of the clubs' providing the extra trick is 39%: if this fails declarer must finesse ◇Q, giving a total of 70%. As the cards lie, a club–diamond squeeze against East will suffice, yet a far superior plan is to play for a combined guard or double squeeze. Declarer cashes ♡A, discarding a diamond, and then cashes ◇A. He returns to hand with a diamond ruff to run the trumps. This will be the four-card ending:

```
♠ —
♡ J
◇ Q
♣ A 3
```

```
♠ 7
♡ —
◇ —
♣ K 9 4
```

Note that declarer must be careful to discard dummy's ♣10. On the lead of the last trump dummy throws ♡J (unless West has thrown ♡Q). This plan will work whenever East has ◇K. If West has ◇K and either ♣J or ♣Q he will be forced to bare the club picture in order to protect his red honours, and declarer makes the thirteenth trick by the finesse of his ♣9. This ending is known as the guard squeeze and the combined chances can be assessed as $87\frac{1}{2}\%$.

This deal occurred in the 1970 Masters' Pairs Championship. Although the top award went to 7 NT—it failed only once—7♠ was a popular contract. However, popular or not, it failed on no less than six occasions, and on another four occasions the declarers in 6♠ failed to make an overtrick!

Teams
Game all
Dealer North

♠ K Q 6 4
♡ Q J 6
♢ 5 4 3
♣ J 10 9

◇A led

```
    N
W       E
    S
```

♠ J 5 3
♡ A K 9 8 5 3
♢ 9
♣ Q 6 4

South manages to buy the contract in three hearts. West starts with the ace and king of diamonds, South ruffing the second round. Two top trumps are cashed, East discarding the seven of clubs on the second round.

How should declarer proceed?

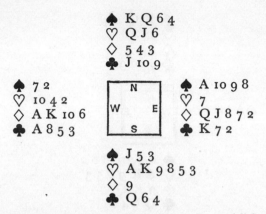

```
                    ♠ K Q 6 4
                    ♡ Q J 6
                    ◇ 5 4 3
                    ♣ J 10 9
   ♠ 7 2          ┌─────────┐      ♠ A 10 9 8
   ♡ 10 4 2       │    N    │      ♡ 7
   ◇ A K 10 6     │ W     E │      ◇ Q J 8 7 2
   ♣ A 8 5 3      │    S    │      ♣ K 7 2
                  └─────────┘
                    ♠ J 5 3
                    ♡ A K 9 8 5 3
                    ◇ 9
                    ♣ Q 6 4
```

Before drawing the last trump declarer must establish tricks in the side-suits—but which black suit should he play first? Many players would make the mistake of playing a spade. This hand is taken from the quarter-finals of the Spingold Trophy, held at the 1966 Summer Nationals in Denver, Colorado. South was one of the world's best technicians, Edgar Kaplan. Appreciating that the danger was a ruff, he saw that he could not avert a club ruff should the clubs be 5–2. However, if he played on spades the defence could duck and thereafter must prevail (declarer either runs short of trumps or sustains a ruff). Kaplan played a club and earned a useful swing.

Teams
Game all
Dealer South

```
              ♠ 5 4 3
              ♡ 8 6 2
              ◇ 8 6 5 4 3
              ♣ 10 7
```

♣A led

```
              N
          W       E
              S
```

```
              ♠ A K 10 8 6 2
              ♡ A K 5
              ◇ A K Q
              ♣ Q
```

Bidding:

SOUTH	WEST	NORTH	EAST
2♣	Double	Pass	Pass
2♠	Pass	3♠	Pass
4♠	Pass	Pass	Pass

West leads the ace and king of clubs. How should South direct the play when he discovers that East has all the missing trumps?

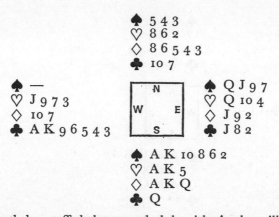

♠ 5 4 3
♡ 8 6 2
◇ 8 6 5 4 3
♣ 10 7

♠ —
♡ J 9 7 3
◇ 10 7
♣ A K 9 6 5 4 3

♠ Q J 9 7
♡ Q 10 4
◇ J 9 2
♣ J 8 2

♠ A K 10 8 6 2
♡ A K 5
◇ A K Q
♣ Q

If South has ruffed the second club with ♠2 he will be unable to redeem his error—as we shall see! The club is ruffed with the ♠6, and ♠A reveals the position. Now three rounds of diamonds are followed by three rounds of hearts. In at trick nine with ♡Q East can do no better than play ♠Q, but declarer counters this move by following with the ♠8. If East now plays a club South must ruff with his carefully preserved ♠2 and take the trick in dummy with ♠4. East's second trump trick is now lost to declarer's tenace.

It will not help East to unblock his hearts and allow West to play the thirteenth. In this event dummy ruffs, and when East overruffs with an honour—it would only delay the endplay to discard his club—South underruffs with ♠8, still preserving that vital ♠2.

One of England's young stars, Irving Rose, showed his fine technique in the Scottish Congress at Turnberry in 1969, when this fascinating hand was dealt in the Pairs Championship.

Pairs
East–West vulnerable
Dealer West

> ♠ K 5 4
> ♡ Q 10 8
> ◇ 7 5 2
> ♣ A Q 7 4

◇K led

```
    N
W       E
    S
```

> ♠ A J 10 9 8 7 6
> ♡ 9
> ◇ Q 6
> ♣ 6 5 3

Bidding:

SOUTH	WEST	NORTH	EAST
	1 NT*	Pass	4♡
4♠	Double	Pass	Pass
Pass			

* 12–14 points.

West leads the king of diamonds against South's contract of four spades doubled, East playing the jack. At trick two West switches to the six of hearts, East winning with the king. Now the ten of diamonds, covered by the queen, goes to West's ace. At trick four West plays the three of diamonds and East the eight. South ruffs, and now has to make the remainder of the tricks if he is to succeed in his contract.

How should he plan the play?

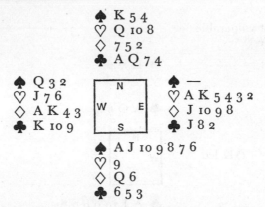

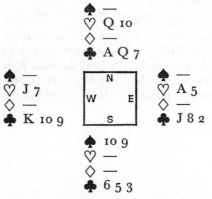

To justify his opening bid of 1 NT and final double West is marked with ♣K and ♠Q. Also, from the play of the heart suit and East's jump to 4♡, it seems that West must have started with ♡ J 7 6 and East with ♡ A K 5 4 3 2. The spades will almost certainly be divided 3–0. Having analysed the distribution it now remains to draw up the plan.

To make the remainder of the tricks declarer will have to rely on an exotic type of heart–club squeeze. He cannot afford the luxury of laying down ♠A, for that would only block the suit in the almost certain event of West's holding ♠ Q x x. It is imperative that declarer should be in his own hand after drawing trumps. Therefore, at trick five ♠J is led and run when West fails to cover. Now, having drawn the trumps, declarer plays a fourth round to arrive at the diagram position. On the lead of ♠10 West has to release a club; otherwise declarer will enter dummy with ♣Q to play ♡Q, pinning West's ♡J. Dummy throws a club and now East is in trouble. He has to keep his hearts intact, otherwise, with the aid of the club finesse, declarer can ruff out his ♡A. So he too parts with a club. Now ♣Q and ♣A leaves South holding a master trump and the thirteenth club.

Teams
Game all
Dealer South

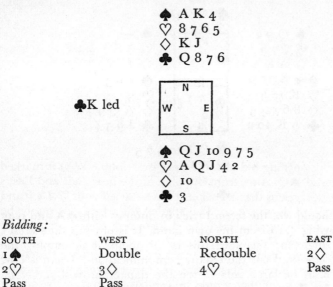

♠ A K 4
♡ 8 7 6 5
◇ K J
♣ Q 8 7 6

♣K led

♠ Q J 10 9 7 5
♡ A Q J 4 2
◇ 10
♣ 3

Bidding:

SOUTH	WEST	NORTH	EAST
1♠	Double	Redouble	2◇
2♡	3◇	4♡	Pass
Pass	Pass		

West leads the king of clubs against South's contract of four hearts, and then switches to the two of spades.

What stratagem should South adopt to avert the impending ruff?

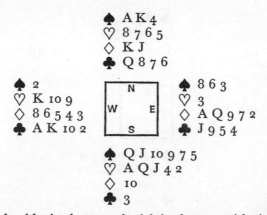

Declarer should win the second trick in dummy with ♠A and play
♣Q, throwing ◊10 from his own hand. It is obvious that West's
♠2 is a singleton; therefore this is the moment to employ the
Scissors Coup—and cut the enemy communications. There is now
no defence. If declarer fails to see the danger he will surely be
defeated, for West, when in with ♡K, will switch to a diamond,
and East will then return a spade for the setting trick.

This hand occurred in the 1969 World Championships in Rio de
Janeiro (France *v*. Italy). The only alteration is that the bidding has
been amended to conform with approach-forcing methods. The
contract was the same in both rooms, but whereas the Italian
declarer went one down (he had no opposition bidding to help him,
and elected to play ♡A and then ♡Q after the spade switch), H.
Svarc, for France, secured a sizeable swing by the play described
above.

Rubber bridge
North–South vulnerable
Dealer South

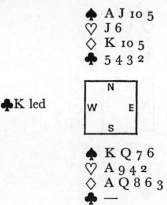

♠ A J 10 5
♡ J 6
◇ K 10 5
♣ 5 4 3 2

♣K led

♠ K Q 7 6
♡ A 9 4 2
◇ A Q 8 6 3
♣ —

West leads the king of clubs against South's optimistic contract of seven spades.

How should declarer plan the play?

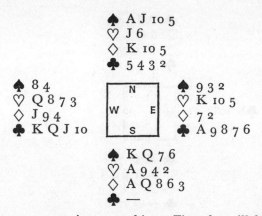

Declarer must appreciate two things. First, he will have to score three ruffs in his own hand, which, together with dummy's four spades, ♡A and five diamond tricks, will bring his total to thirteen. Secondly, in order to achieve this he will require three entries to dummy: two to ruff clubs and one to draw trumps. As there will be only one trump entry he will need *two* diamond entries, which entails the assumption that West holds ♢J.

The opening lead is ruffed and a diamond played to dummy's ♢10. A club ruff, ♢K and a third club ruff leaves only the mopping-up operation of drawing trumps and discarding three heart losers from his own hand.

Teams
Game all
Dealer North

♠ Q J 5 3
♡ 10 7 5
◇ A K 9
♣ K 6 2

♠6 led

```
      N
  W       E
      S
```

♠ 10 4
♡ A K 9 8 3 2
◇ 4
♣ A Q 10 8

Bidding:

SOUTH	WEST	NORTH	EAST
		1♣	1♠
2♡	Pass	2 NT	Pass
4♣	Pass	4♡	Pass
4♠	Pass	5♡	Pass
Pass	Pass		

The bidding has the flavour of Continental excitability, but we are concerned with the play.

West leads the six of spades against South's contract of five hearts. East wins with the king, cashes the ace of spades, on which West follows with the two, and then switches to the seven of clubs.

How should South proceed?

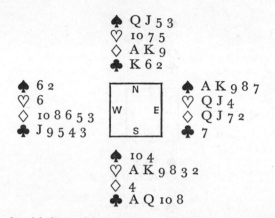

♠ Q J 5 3
♡ 10 7 5
◇ A K 9
♣ K 6 2

♠ 6 2
♡ 6
◇ 10 8 6 5 3
♣ J 9 5 4 3

♠ A K 9 8 7
♡ Q J 4
◇ Q J 7 2
♣ 7

♠ 10 4
♡ A K 9 8 3 2
◇ 4
♣ A Q 10 8

Declarer should direct his attention to this question: why did East, who is presumably marked with five spades, not continue with a third spade? If West has any heart honour this would spell instant defeat. The conclusion that South should reach is that East must hold both ♡Q and ♡J and is fearful of exposing the position. Thus declarer should win the club switch in dummy and play ♡10— letting it run if East fails to cover.

This hand occurred in the European Championships at Palermo, Britain *v.* Austria. In the open room Terence Reese (South) and Boris Schapiro (North) played in 3NT and Schapiro had no difficulty in collecting ten tricks after an initial spade lead. In the closed room the British East–West pair were B. Franks (East) and J. Lazarus (West). Defending against 5♡, Frank could see that a third round of spades would almost certainly let the cat out of the bag, so he switched to a club. There was an anxious moment as a trump was played from dummy, but the Austrian declarer failed to draw the right inference and the contract was defeated by one trick.

Rubber bridge
Game all
Dealer East

$\spadesuit$ 4
$\heartsuit$ Q 7 2
$\diamondsuit$ Q 6 5 2
$\clubsuit$ 9 8 7 6 4

$\spadesuit$ 10 led

```
   N
W     E
   S
```

$\spadesuit$ A 7 2
$\heartsuit$ A J 5 3
$\diamondsuit$ A K 9 8 7
$\clubsuit$ 3

Bidding:

SOUTH	WEST	NORTH	EAST
			3$\spadesuit$
Double	Pass	4$\spadesuit$!	Pass
6$\diamondsuit$	Pass	Pass	Pass

An exotic sequence, where North cannot be accused of under-bidding! West leads the ten of spades against South's contract of six diamonds.

Prospects do not look bright, but to give himself any chance South should assume that East holds K x in hearts. On this basis, how should he plan the play?

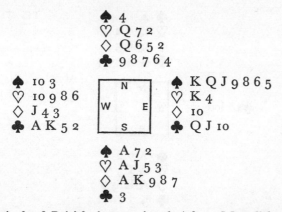

```
                        ♠ 4
                        ♡ Q 7 2
                        ◇ Q 6 5 2
                        ♣ 9 8 7 6 4

   ♠ 10 3          N          ♠ K Q J 9 8 6 5
   ♡ 10 9 8 6                 ♡ K 4
   ◇ J 4 3      W      E      ◇ 10
   ♣ A K 5 2       S          ♣ Q J 10

                        ♠ A 7 2
                        ♡ A J 5 3
                        ◇ A K 9 8 7
                        ♣ 3
```

It was typical of British international Adam Meredith that he showed no distress at the exposure of North's disappointing dummy. Equally typical were the facility with which he realized that East had to be placed with ♡ K x, and the perfection of his technique.

In order to prepare the ground for a crossruff and squeeze position he won the first trick with ♠A and exited with a club. East won and, in an attempt to force the dummy, returned a spade (nothing else would be better). Dummy ruffed and a club was ruffed in hand. ◇A was cashed and declarer's last spade led towards dummy. At this point West was in trouble and in order to avoid being squeezed out of either heart or club control he had to follow with a trump! Dummy overruffed and returned a small heart; ♡J and ♡A took the next two tricks. A heart to the ♡Q was followed by a club ruff, heart ruff and club ruff. ◇K scored the thirteenth trick.

Teams
North–South vulnerable
Dealer East

♠ K Q 4
♡ A K 6 5
◇ 9 6 2
♣ Q 5 4

♠J led

```
      N
 W        E
      S
```

♠ 7 5 2
♡ Q 3
◇ A K 8
♣ K J 10 9 3

Bidding:

SOUTH	WEST	NORTH	EAST
			Pass
1♣	Pass	1♡	Pass
1 NT	Pass	3 NT	Pass
Pass	Pass		

West leads the jack of spades against South's contract of three no trumps.

What is the best line of play?

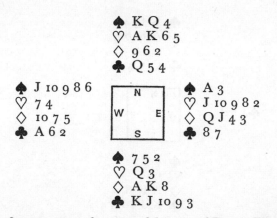

```
          ♠ K Q 4
          ♡ A K 6 5
          ◇ 9 6 2
          ♣ Q 5 4
♠ J 10 9 8 6    ┌─────┐    ♠ A 3
♡ 7 4           │  N  │    ♡ J 10 9 8 2
◇ 10 7 5        │ W E │    ◇ Q J 4 3
♣ A 6 2         │  S  │    ♣ 8 7
                └─────┘
          ♠ 7 5 2
          ♡ Q 3
          ◇ A K 8
          ♣ K J 10 9 3
```

In the 1969–70 season the powerful team of Reese, Flint, Cansino, Milford, Rose and Cooke made an early exit from the Gold Cup. On the hand above one of our players contributed a spade picture at trick one and was subsequently defeated. The same contract played by North in the other room presented no problems. In the 'friendly' discussion after the match declarer was 'arraigned before his peers'. He pleaded that his play was normal and that to duck savours of *ex post facto* analysis. Reese, for the prosecution, pointed out that to duck would lose only when West had led from ♠ A J 10 x x and ♣A. As West had not overcalled with 1♠, not vulnerable against vulnerable opponents, this was an improbable holding. The jury delivered their verdict immediately: 'Guilty as charged.'

Rubber bridge
Game all
Dealer South

♠ J 8 7 2
♡ A K J
◇ K Q 8 5
♣ 10 5

♣K led

```
    N
W       E
    S
```

♠ A K 10 6 4
♡ Q 3
◇ A J 9
♣ A 6 4

West leads the king of clubs against South's contract of six spades. South wins the opening lead and lays down the ace and king of trumps, East following to the first round but discarding the two of hearts on the second.

How should declarer continue from here?

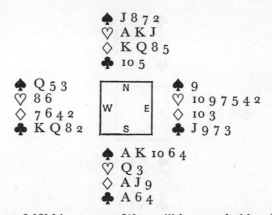

♠ J 8 7 2
♡ A K J
◇ K Q 8 5
♣ 10 5

♠ Q 5 3   ♠ 9
♡ 8 6   ♡ 10 9 7 5 4 2
◇ 7 6 4 2   ◇ 10 3
♣ K Q 8 2   ♣ J 9 7 3

♠ A K 10 6 4
♡ Q 3
◇ A J 9
♣ A 6 4

If South is to fulfil his contract West will have to hold at least three diamonds, therefore the diamonds must be tackled *before* the hearts. If the diamonds divide 3–3 then South will take a discard on the hearts before playing the thirteenth diamond. But if West happens to hold four diamonds—as is the case here—then declarer disposes of one of his club losers before playing on hearts.

When this hand occurred declarer, who was noted for his lessons to the weaker brethren, played the red suits in the wrong order. At the end of the hand his face was as red as the suits he had misplayed!

Rubber bridge
Love all
Dealer South

```
              ♠ J 8 2
              ♡ 10 6 4
              ◇ A 4 3 2
              ♣ J 8 4

              ┌─────────┐
              │    N    │
  ♡K led      │ W     E │
              │    S    │
              └─────────┘

              ♠ A K 9 7 5 4 3
              ♡ J 7 5
              ◇ 9
              ♣ A 5
```

Without opposition bidding South reaches the optimistic contract of four spades. West leads the king of hearts and, encouraged by his partner's nine, continues with the queen. At trick three West switches to the six of spades, East following with the queen.

What play will give declarer the best chance for this unlikely contract?

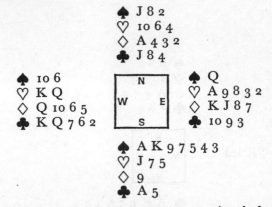

Swiss international Pietro Bernasconi appreciated the necessity of the key play—♣5 at trick four! There are three good reasons for making this play. To set the stage for the final act; to give West, should he win the trick, an easy exit card—♠10; and to avoid giving East an opportunity to signal for a diamond switch.

The play went exactly as Bernasconi foresaw, West winning the club and exiting with ♠10. Four more trumps and ♣A produced this position:

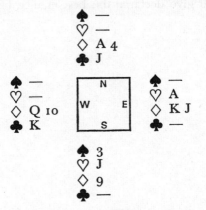

On ♠3 West had to let go ♢10. The pressure now turned on East, dummy throwing ♣J. East had to retain ♡A so he too threw a diamond. Dummy's ♢4 now became the twelfth trick.

Pairs
Game all
Dealer South

```
              ♠ K 3
              ♡ K Q 8 4
              ◇ A 8 4
              ♣ 6 4 3 2

                  ┌─────────┐
                  │    N    │
  ♠J led          │ W     E │
                  │    S    │
                  └─────────┘

              ♠ A Q
              ♡ A J 6
              ◇ K Q 10 9 3
              ♣ A 7 5
```

West leads the jack of spades against South's contract of six no trumps.

How should South plan the play?

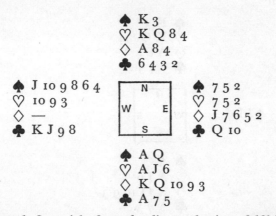

♠ K 3
♡ K Q 8 4
◇ A 8 4
♣ 6 4 3 2

♠ J 10 9 8 6 4
♡ 10 9 3
◇ —
♣ K J 9 8

♠ 7 5 2
♡ 7 5 2
◇ J 7 6 5 2
♣ Q 10

♠ A Q
♡ A J 6
◇ K Q 10 9 3
♣ A 7 5

South needs five tricks from the diamond suit to fulfil his contract. He must be careful therefore to play ◇3 from his own hand to dummy's ◇A. If West holds all the missing diamonds, or four to the ◇J, there is no practical method of bringing in the suit without loss. For this reason declarer must make provision for East holding five diamonds: once he has led small to the ace two finesses will enable declarer to take five tricks in the suit.

This hand was played in the final of the London Flitch, the married couples' championship, in the mid-sixties. One of the few successful Souths was a wife who tried hard to remember all the instructions her husband had given her. Already conscious that she had broken Rule One, which decreed that he played all the hands, she tried desperately to think what he had said about suit combinations missing one honour. 'Was it a case of leading towards the length?' she muttered, and then aloud, 'It is no use, I can't remember.' Suddenly ◇3 was on the table and the contract safely in the bag!

Teams
Game all
Dealer West

```
                        ♠ A 8 4 2
                        ♡ 9 6 3
                        ◇ J 6 2
                        ♣ Q J 4
```

```
                  ┌───────────┐
                  │     N     │
  ◇8 led          │ W       E │
                  │     S     │
                  └───────────┘
```

```
                        ♠ K 3
                        ♡ A K 10 8 7 4
                        ◇ 9 5
                        ♣ A 7 5
```

Bidding:

SOUTH	WEST	NORTH	EAST
	Pass	Pass	1 ◇
2 ♡	Pass	3 ♡	3 ♣
4 ♡	Double	Pass	Pass
Pass			

West leads the eight of diamonds. East takes two top diamonds and plays a third round—the ace. West overruffs the eight of hearts with the jack and switches to the seven of spades. Declarer wins and draws the remaining trumps, discovering that West held ♡ Q J 2 originally.

How should he continue?

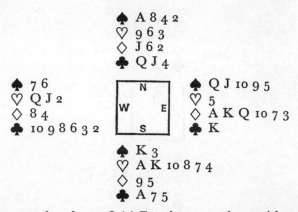

Declarer must lay down ♣A! East has turned up with seven red cards and almost certainly holds five spades, leaving him with a lone club. It cannot possibly help declarer to finesse, for that must be the one certain way of losing a trick in the suit—whatever the distribution.

Terence Reese played this hand in the second World Olympiad in New York, 1964. At the critical stage, instead of playing ♣A, he said, 'I will have to concede a club unless the king of clubs is bare.' Our opponents never recovered their morale. Little did they realize that Reese knew the clubs were 6–1 and had a shrewd idea that ♣K might be singleton.

Pairs
Love all
Dealer South

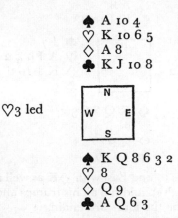

♠ A 10 4
♡ K 10 6 5
◇ A 8
♣ K J 10 8

♡3 led

♠ K Q 8 6 3 2
♡ 8
◇ Q 9
♣ A Q 6 3

Perhaps the method of scoring is responsible for the inferior contract of six spades. Of course, six clubs would normally be a safer proposition. Against six spades West leads the three of hearts, dummy plays low and East wins with the nine. East switches to a low spade won by dummy's ten. On the ace of spades West throws the two of diamonds. A low heart is ruffed at trick four, East following with the two and West with the seven.

How should declarer proceed?

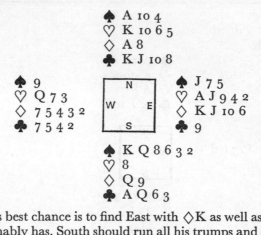

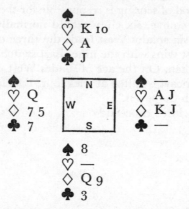

Declarer's best chance is to find East with ◇K as well as ♡A, which he presumably has. South should run all his trumps and clubs except one of each. This will be the four-card ending:

A club to dummy's ♣J squeezes East. If he parts with a heart, South will ruff a heart and enter dummy with ◇A to enjoy the master heart. If East discards a diamond ◇A is cashed, setting up declarer's ◇Q.

This hand is a good example of the artistry of Mimmo d'Alelio, a member of the invincible Italian Blue Team, who duly landed his contract of 6♠.

Rubber bridge
North–South vulnerable
Dealer North

```
              ♠ 8 5
              ♡ A 10 8 6 4
              ◇ A 6 3
              ♣ Q 10 3

                ┌─────────┐
                │    N    │
◇2 led          │ W     E │
                │    S    │
                └─────────┘

              ♠ K 7 2
              ♡ K Q 9 5
              ◇ Q J 5 4
              ♣ A 8
```

Bidding:

SOUTH	WEST	NORTH	EAST
		Pass	Pass
1♡	Pass	3♡	Pass
4♡	Pass	Pass	Pass

West leads the two of diamonds against South's contract of four hearts. East wins with the king and returns the three of spades.

How should declarer plan the play?

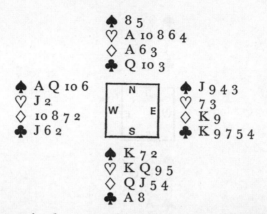

```
                  ♠ 8 5
                  ♡ A 10 8 6 4
                  ◇ A 6 3
                  ♣ Q 10 3
♠ A Q 10 6                          ♠ J 9 4 3
♡ J 2            ┌─────────┐        ♡ 7 3
◇ 10 8 7 2      │    N    │        ◇ K 9
♣ J 6 2         │  W   E  │        ♣ K 9 7 5 4
                 │    S    │
                 └─────────┘
                  ♠ K 7 2
                  ♡ K Q 9 5
                  ◇ Q J 5 4
                  ♣ A 8
```

South must resist the temptation of going up with ♠K. West wins with ♠10 but is now powerless. If he cashes ♠A South will simply win the fourth trick, draw trumps and discard two clubs from dummy. If ♠A is not cashed then the spade loser will be discarded on declarer's long diamond.

When this hand was played South went up with ♠K, and duly failed when he subsequently had to lose a club trick. He carefully explained to his partner that the only hope he had of making ♠K was to contribute it at once. He went on to observe that East could have made certain of defeating the contract by leading ♠J. 'What a shame we were not defending,' replied his partner acidly, 'you would then have had a real opportunity to display your acumen.'

Rubber bridge
Love all
Dealer North

♠ A 5
♡ Q 9 4
◇ A K 9 5 3
♣ 9 5 2

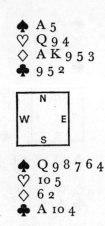

♣K led

♠ Q 9 8 7 6 4
♡ 10 5
◇ 6 2
♣ A 10 4

Bidding :

SOUTH	WEST	NORTH	EAST
		1 ◇	Pass
1 ♠	1 NT	Pass	Pass
2 ♠	Pass	Pass	Pass

West leads the king of clubs against South's contract of two spades.
How should declarer plan the play?

A Royal Sacrifice

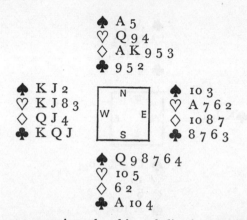

```
                          ♠ A 5
                          ♡ Q 9 4
                          ◇ A K 9 5 3
                          ♣ 9 5 2
   ♠ K J 2                              ♠ 10 3
   ♡ K J 8 3          N                 ♡ A 7 6 2
   ◇ Q J 4        W        E            ◇ 10 8 7
   ♣ K Q J            S                 ♣ 8 7 6 3
                          ♠ Q 9 8 7 6 4
                          ♡ 10 5
                          ◇ 6 2
                          ♣ A 10 4
```

Declarer must appreciate that his task lies in avoiding the loss of two clubs, two hearts and two spades. He wins ♣A and plays three rounds of diamonds, ruffing the third round. ♠Q follows, which forces West to cover. Now a diamond from dummy gives East a choice of plays: to ruff or discard. In either case South disposes of a club loser. If East ruffs, South will subsequently lose two hearts, one club and one spade. If East discards West must ruff and the same losers will be lost when South crashes the master spades together. If South fails to play precisely ♠Q at trick five the contract will be lost, since West must make two spade tricks while East can kill the diamond lead from dummy.

The key to declarer's fine play was the assumption that West's hand was likely to be strong and balanced to justify his overcall.

Teams
North–South vulnerable
Dealer South

　　　　　　　　　♠ A 8 7
　　　　　　　　　♡ A Q 7 4
　　　　　　　　　◇ A K
　　　　　　　　　♣ Q J 9 6

♣K led

```
        N
   W         E
        S
```

　　　　　　　　　♠ Q 10 5 3 2
　　　　　　　　　♡ 10
　　　　　　　　　◇ J 10 8 3 2
　　　　　　　　　♣ 4 3

Bidding:

SOUTH	WEST	NORTH	EAST
Pass	Pass	1 ♡	Pass
Pass	1 NT	Double	Pass
2 ♠	Pass	3 ♣	Pass
4 ♠	Pass	Pass	Pass

West leads the king of clubs against South's contract of four spades. When his partner plays the two he switches to a low heart. Declarer wins with the ace, cashes two top diamonds, ruffs a heart, ruffs a diamond—West playing the queen—and then plays ace and another spade. On the first round of spades both defenders play low. On the second round East plays the nine.

Which card should South play and why?

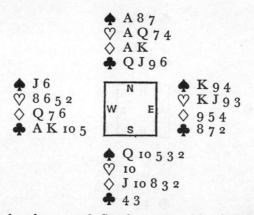

♠ A 8 7
♡ A Q 7 4
◇ A K
♣ Q J 9 6

♠ J 6
♡ 8 6 5 2
◇ Q 7 6
♣ A K 10 5

♠ K 9 4
♡ K J 9 3
◇ 9 5 4
♣ 8 7 2

♠ Q 10 5 3 2
♡ 10
◇ J 10 8 3 2
♣ 4 3

When this hand occurred, South at one table played ♠10 at trick eight and claimed that he had made an unlucky guess. In fact the score of −100 instead of +620 was due to sheer carelessness. Did you remember the bidding? South in the other room was Willie Coyle, the Scottish international, who reflected on the bidding before playing to the second round of spades. He recalled that West passed originally, yet he had already shown up with an ace, a king and a queen. With ♠K as well he would surely have opened, especially at favourable vulnerability. As to the position of ♠J, this was almost certainly marked with West since his reopening bid was 1 NT. Willie Coyle is not guilty of this type of error, and unhesitatingly played ♠Q.

Pairs
North–South vulnerable
Dealer West

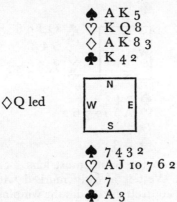

♠ A K 5
♡ K Q 8
◇ A K 8 3
♣ K 4 2

◇Q led

N
W   E
S

♠ 7 4 3 2
♡ A J 10 7 6 2
◇ 7
♣ A 3

After West has opened the bidding with three diamonds South becomes the declarer in seven no trumps. West leads the queen of diamonds.

How should declarer plan the play?

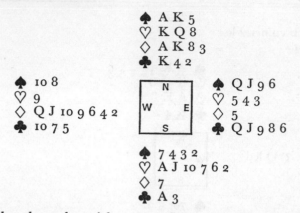

With only twelve tricks on top South must look for a squeeze to develop the thirteenth. West is already marked with control in diamonds so if only East controls the spades the winning plan should be apparent. After ◇ A K, five top hearts, ♠ A K and ♣A, this is the position:

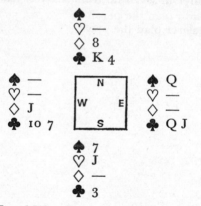

South plays ♡J and West has to part with a club. Dummy discards ◇8 and now East is squeezed. Dummy's ♣4 takes the thirteenth trick.

It would of course be futile to attempt the alternative double squeeze using spades as the pivotal suit, as then the club menace would be misplaced—that is, East discards after dummy.

Rubber bridge
Game all
Dealer South

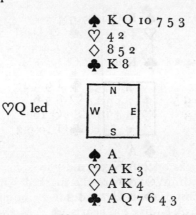

♠ K Q 10 7 5 3
♡ 4 2
◇ 8 5 2
♣ K 8

♡Q led

N
W E
S

♠ A
♡ A K 3
◇ A K 4
♣ A Q 7 6 4 3

West leads the queen of hearts against South's unambitious contract of six no trumps.

How should South plan the play?

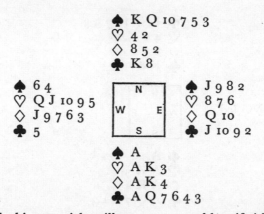

♠ K Q 10 7 5 3
♡ 4 2
◇ 8 5 2
♣ K 8

♠ 6 4
♡ Q J 10 9 5
◇ J 9 7 6 3
♣ 5

♠ J 9 8 2
♡ 8 7 6
◇ Q 10
♣ J 10 9 2

♠ A
♡ A K 3
◇ A K 4
♣ A Q 7 6 4 3

Although thirteen tricks will present no problem if either black suit breaks favourably, declarer should invest in a small insurance policy to guard against distributional storms. He should win the heart lead in hand, cash ♠A and duck a club. As the cards lie, East wins this trick, but declarer can now take the balance. It will be observed that the safety play is essential where either defender holds four clubs together with ♠Jxxx.

Rubber bridge
Love all
Dealer North

                    ♠ Q J
                    ♡ A K Q 9 8
                    ◇ K
                    ♣ A K 9 5 3

    ♣ 10 led   ┌─────────┐
                    │   N   │
                    │ W   E │
                    │   S   │
                    └─────────┘

                    ♠ A K 8 5 4
                    ♡ 10 5
                    ◇ Q 8 7 4
                    ♣ 6 4

West leads the ten of clubs against South's contract of six spades.

How should South plan the play to give himself the best chance of making his contract?

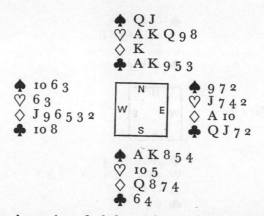

♠ Q J
♡ A K Q 9 8
♢ K
♣ A K 9 5 3

♠ 10 6 3
♡ 6 3
♢ J 9 6 5 3 2
♣ 10 8

♠ 9 7 2
♡ J 7 4 2
♢ A 10
♣ Q J 7 2

♠ A K 8 5 4
♡ 10 5
♢ Q 8 7 4
♣ 6 4

The best chance is to find the *spades* 3–3 (36%)—not an attractive proposition. Yet the odds only get worse if you try to improve on the suggested line. Winning the club in dummy declarer should cash ♡A followed by the ♠ Q J and ♡K. He should then ruff ♡8 with ♠A and cash the ♠K. When the spades fall his problems are over.

The lead of ♣10 makes it unlikely that this suit will divide evenly. There is, however, the possibility of the hearts dividing 3–3 while the spades are 4–2. If this is the position declarer can ruff the third heart with a low spade. However, this line of play is clearly inferior to the recommended approach since there is no guarantee that declarer will succeed even if the major suits are so divided (hearts 3–3 and spades 4–2) because of the additional factor that unless ♢A is held by the hand with a doubleton club the declarer will never enjoy his diamond trick. Playing for the 3–3 spade break it is immaterial who holds ♢A or how the clubs are divided.

Pairs
Love all
Dealer South

♠ A K 10 2
♡ J 7
◇ 9 8 2
♣ A K J 6

◇J led

```
    N
W       E
    S
```

♠ J 8 6
♡ A K 6 5 4 3 2
◇ A 10
♣ 10

Bidding :

SOUTH	WEST	NORTH	EAST
1♡	Pass	1♠	2◇
4♡	Pass	4 NT	Pass
5♡	Pass	6♡	Pass
Pass	Pass		

West leads the jack of diamonds against South's contract of six hearts. South wins with the ace and cashes a top heart, East playing the queen. Declarer can now see twelve tricks and sets about trying to make thirteen. A heart to dummy's jack, East throwing a diamond, and then the ace of clubs and a club ruff provides some revealing information when East discards another diamond on the second club.

How should South proceed?

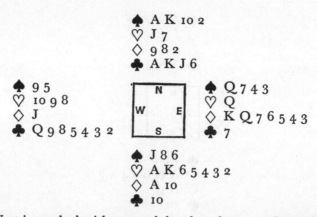

♠ A K 10 2
♡ J 7
◇ 9 8 2
♣ A K J 6

♠ 9 5
♡ 10 9 8
◇ J
♣ Q 9 8 5 4 3 2

♠ Q 7 4 3
♡ Q
◇ K Q 7 6 5 4 3
♣ 7

♠ J 8 6
♡ A K 6 5 4 3 2
◇ A 10
♣ 10

As West is marked with seven clubs, three hearts and one diamond he cannot hold more than two spades. Therefore if he holds ♠Q it will drop. Alternatively, if East holds ♠Q he can be squeezed in spades and diamonds providing South discards a *spade* from his hand and *not* ◇10. The last trump is drawn and then dummy is entered with a top spade. On ♣K South discards a spade and the South hand is re-entered with a club ruff. East cannot resist the pressure exerted by declarer's remaining trumps.

Peter Pender, the American star, displayed his flair for the pairs method of scoring when he played as described above in the final of the 1966 West Coast Pairs Championship in Los Angeles. He won this event from a field of over 700 pairs.

Teams
North–South vulnerable
Dealer South

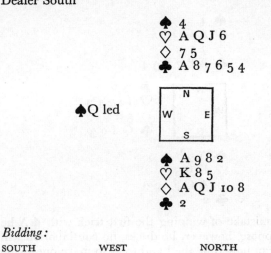

♠ 4
♡ A Q J 6
◇ 7 5
♣ A 8 7 6 5 4

♠ Q led

♠ A 9 8 2
♡ K 8 5
◇ A Q J 10 8
♣ 2

Bidding:

SOUTH	WEST	NORTH	EAST
1 ◇	1 ♠	2 ♣	2 ♠
3 ◇	Pass	3 ♡	Pass
3 ♠	Pass	4 ◇	Pass
5 ◇	Pass	Pass	Pass

West leads the queen of spades against South's contract of five diamonds.

How should declarer plan the play?

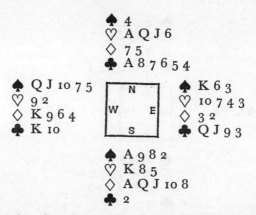

```
              ♠ 4
              ♡ A Q J 6
              ◇ 7 5
              ♣ A 8 7 6 5 4
♠ Q J 10 7 5              ♠ K 6 3
♡ 9 2          N         ♡ 10 7 4 3
◇ K 9 6 4    W   E       ◇ 3 2
♣ K 10          S         ♣ Q J 9 3
              ♠ A 9 8 2
              ♡ K 8 5
              ◇ A Q J 10 8
              ♣ 2
```

If South makes the mistake of winning the first trick with ♠A he will lose control. Suppose, however, he ducks, no continuation will embarrass him. He can now time the hand so as to make one spade ruff, four diamonds, four hearts, one spade and one club—a total of eleven tricks.

This hand was played in a Gold Cup match by J. C. H. Marx, ex-European Champion and one of the founders of the Acol System. Although the contract was the same in the other room the rival declarer did not find Marx's winning line.

Teams
East–West vulnerable
Dealer South

$\spadesuit$ Q 5 4
$\heartsuit$ 8 4 2
$\diamondsuit$ A 10 2
$\clubsuit$ K Q 9 6

$\diamondsuit$K led

```
    N
W       E
    S
```

$\spadesuit$ A K 2
$\heartsuit$ A K 10 9 6 5
$\diamondsuit$ J
$\clubsuit$ A 7 4

South arrives in six hearts and West leads the king of diamonds, won by the ace. When a heart is led from dummy East discards a diamond.

How should declarer proceed?

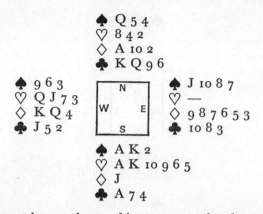

```
                ♠ Q 5 4
                ♡ 8 4 2
                ◇ A 10 2
                ♣ K Q 9 6
♠ 9 6 3          ┌─────────┐      ♠ J 10 8 7
♡ Q J 7 3        │    N    │      ♡ —
◇ K Q 4        W │         │ E    ◇ 9 8 7 6 5 3
♣ J 5 2          │    S    │      ♣ 10 8 3
                 └─────────┘
                ♠ A K 2
                ♡ A K 10 9 6 5
                ◇ J
                ♣ A 7 4
```

Declarer must plan to shorten his trumps so that he can endplay West. The ♡A takes the second trick, then, entering dummy twice, he ruffs two diamonds, cashes the four top black suit winners and, at trick eleven, plays ♡10. West wins this trick but has to concede the last two to South.

This hand occurred in the 1969 British Trials for the European Championships. Three Souths made 6♡. One arrived in 7♣— making ten tricks. One played in 7♡ doubled and was apparently so depressed when he saw the trump break that he just conceded *two* down. At the last table the declarer, one of the best young players in the country, was in the popular contract of 6♡ and conceded one down as soon as East discarded on the first round of trumps!

Assuredly declarer needs to find West with the right distribution in the side-suits, but it was only justice that this was so in view of the harsh trump break.

Rubber bridge
East–West vulnerable
Dealer West

```
              ♠ 3
              ♡ 10 5
              ◇ J 7 3
              ♣ A Q J 7 4 3 2

              ┌───N───┐
◇5 led        W       E
              └───S───┘

              ♠ K Q J 4 2
              ♡ A Q J 4
              ◇ K 8 2
              ♣ K
```

Bidding:

SOUTH	WEST	NORTH	EAST
	1♡	Pass	Pass
Double	2◇	3♣	Pass
3 NT	Pass	Pass	Pass

West leads the five of diamonds against South's contract of three no trumps. Declarer plays the jack from dummy which holds the trick. A spade is played at trick two to South's king and West's ace. West cashes the ace of diamonds—East following with the nine—and plays the four of diamonds, East discarding the three of hearts.

How should declarer plan the play?

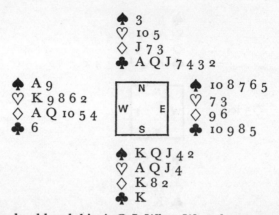

Declarer should cash his ♠ Q J. When West shows out on the third round of spades the count is practically complete. It is fair to infer that West has at least five hearts and he has already shown up with five diamonds and two spades, therefore he cannot have more than one club. Once declarer has appreciated this fact the remainder of the play is simple. He cashes ♣K and ♡A and then exits with a spade—using East as a stepping-stone to dummy's club winners.

This hand occurred in November 1970 in London during a session of high-stake rubber bridge, and the contract was made in the manner described. An interesting point about this deal is that there is virtually no defence to beat the contract. It will be noticed that if East discards a spade instead of the heart South makes nine tricks by establishing the long spade.

Pairs
Love all
Dealer East

♠ 5
♡ 10 9 6 5 4
◇ J 8 7 4
♣ Q 4 2

♡3 led

```
      N
  W       E
      S
```

♠ A 9 4 3
♡ Q
◇ A K 10 9 6 5
♣ A 9

Bidding:

SOUTH	WEST	NORTH	EAST
			1 ♡
Double	1 ♠	Pass	2 ♣
3 ◇	3 ♣	4 ◇	Pass
5 ◇	Pass	Pass	Pass

West leads the three of hearts against South's contract of five diamonds. East wins with the king and switches to the two of diamonds. South plays the ace and West the three.

How should declarer plan the play?

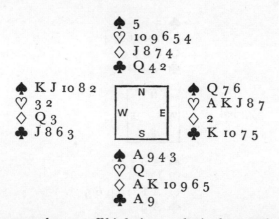

♠ 5
♡ 10 9 6 5 4
◇ J 8 7 4
♣ Q 4 2

♠ K J 10 8 2   ♠ Q 7 6
♡ 3 2   ♡ A K J 8 7
◇ Q 3   ◇ 2
♣ J 8 6 3   ♣ K 10 7 5

♠ A 9 4 3
♡ Q
◇ A K 10 9 6 5
♣ A 9

Declarer must plan to ruff his losing spades in dummy, but doubtless West has ◇Q, which creates considerable problems of re-entry to hand. South must plot his course right through to the point where he has ruffed his spades and can then draw the last trump. ♠A and a spade ruff should be followed by the ♣Q. When East covers he must be allowed to hold this trick. The rest is plain sailing. The heart continuation is ruffed and followed by spade ruff, ♣A, spade ruff, club ruff and ◇K.

When this hand was played in the 1964 Masters' Pairs most declarers failed to see the danger in time, woodenly returning to hand twice via ♣A and a heart ruff. But now, at the critical point, the lead was in dummy and declarer had to play a club or a heart. In either case there was no way to prevent the promotion of West's ◇Q.

Rubber bridge
Love all
Dealer South

              ♠ A 8 4 2
              ♡ K J 9
              ♢ J 8 4
              ♣ A 6 4

♠K led
```
        N
   W        E
        S
```

              ♠ J
              ♡ A Q 8 6 3
              ♢ A K 3
              ♣ K 7 5 2

West leads the king of spades against South's contract of six hearts.
It is clear that the gods will have to be on declarer's side if he is to
succeed.

How should South plan the play?

A Nod from the Gods

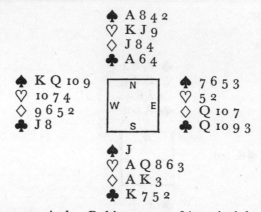

The declarer was Arthur Robinson, one of America's leading players, whose friends claim that he is as lucky as he is skilful. With only ten tricks on top the first thing for declarer to appreciate is that a dummy-reversal play will yield one extra trick—although the finesse against ♡10 will be essential because of the shortage of entries. And the twelfth trick? That will have to come from a minor-suit squeeze should the clubs not break. So South wins the ♠A and ruffs a spade. He ducks a club to rectify the count. The defence returns a club (nothing is better), which he wins with the ♣A. He ruffs a second spade with ♡A, returns to dummy with ♡J and ruffs dummy's last spade with ♡Q. He cashes ◇ A K (Vienna Coup) and now comes the moment of truth as dummy's ♡9 is played on West's ♡7. When it holds the position is:

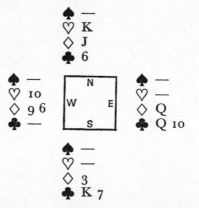

The last trump is played, and East's discomfiture is only surpassed by South's pleasure.

Pairs
North–South vulnerable
Dealer South

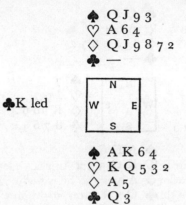

♠ Q J 9 3
♡ A 6 4
◇ Q J 9 8 7 2
♣ —

♣ K led

N
W   E
S

♠ A K 6 4
♡ K Q 5 3 2
◇ A 5
♣ Q 3

Against South's contract of six spades West leads the king of clubs. Dummy ruffs and plays the queen and jack of spades, East discarding a small club on the second round. At trick four declarer runs the queen of diamonds, which holds.

How should he continue?

The Sword of Damocles

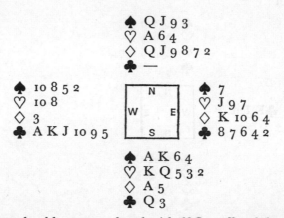

♠ Q J 9 3
♡ A 6 4
◇ Q J 9 8 7 2
♣ —

♠ 10 8 5 2
♡ 10 8
◇ 3
♣ A K J 10 9 5

N
W   E
S

♠ 7
♡ J 9 7
◇ K 10 6 4
♣ 8 7 6 4 2

♠ A K 6 4
♡ K Q 5 3 2
◇ A 5
♣ Q 3

Declarer should return to hand with ♡Q, ruff a club, play a heart
to the ♡K, draw trumps and claim thirteen tricks. Why shouldn't
he return to hand once with ◇A? Because he needs the hearts to be
3–2 to succeed in his contract (unless East has specifically ◇ K x).
He should assume, therefore, that the hearts are 3–2, and not take
a chance on the diamond break, which is immaterial.

This hand occurred in a National Pairs final back in the fifties.
The successful South was the well-known Lancashire player and
British international Ben Franks. Some declarers, not appreciating
the factors involved with the break in the red suits, tried to return
to hand with ◇A. West promptly ruffed and led a trump, holding
declarer to eleven tricks.

Teams
Game all
Dealer West

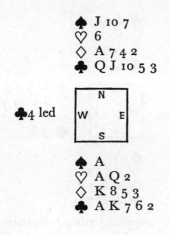

♠ J 10 7
♡ 6
◇ A 7 4 2
♣ Q J 10 5 3

♣4 led

♠ A
♡ A Q 2
◇ K 8 5 3
♣ A K 7 6 2

Bidding:

SOUTH	WEST	NORTH	EAST
	Pass	Pass	Pass
1♣	Pass	3♣	Pass
6♣	Pass	Pass	Pass

West leads the four of clubs against South's contract of six clubs,
East following suit.

How should declarer plan the play?

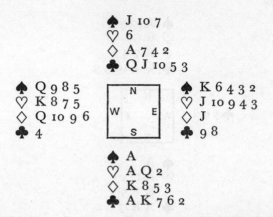

♠ J 10 7
♡ 6
◇ A 7 4 2
♣ Q J 10 5 3

♠ Q 9 8 5   ♠ K 6 4 3 2
♡ K 8 7 5   ♡ J 10 9 4 3
◇ Q 10 9 6   ◇ J
♣ 4   ♣ 9 8

♠ A
♡ A Q 2
◇ K 8 5 3
♣ A K 7 6 2

South should draw the outstanding trump, eliminate the major suits and then play a low diamond from both hands. Unless one hand holds all the diamonds, or ◇ Q J 10 9 precisely, the contract is assured.

Rubber bridge
East–West vulnerable
Dealer East

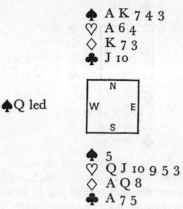

♠ A K 7 4 3
♡ A 6 4
◇ K 7 3
♣ J 10

♠Q led

N
W   E
S

♠ 5
♡ Q J 10 9 5 3
◇ A Q 8
♣ A 7 5

West leads the queen of spades against South's contract of six hearts.

How should declarer continue? If East is void in hearts and West has five spades has declarer any chance of making his contract?

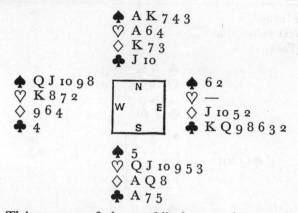

Georges Théron, one of the world's best analysts, gave a fine demonstration of technique when he played this hand in Paris in the early sixties. At trick two normal technique is to cash the ♠K, discarding a club from hand, and continue with a spade ruff. Visions of establishing the long spade are shattered by East's discard of the ♣9. The contract appears to hang on the heart finesse, but South suffers a further rude shock when East discards a second club on ♡Q. The ♡J is followed by three rounds of diamonds ending in dummy and a further spade ruff. The position is now:

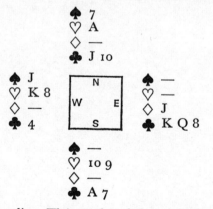

Arriving at this ending, Théron played ♣A and another club. West discarded his ♠J on the second club, but when his partner had to lead to trick twelve West's 'sure trump trick' was smothered into oblivion.

Rubber bridge
Game all
Dealer South

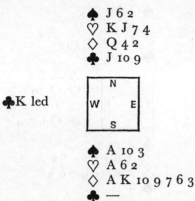

♠ J 6 2
♡ K J 7 4
◇ Q 4 2
♣ J 10 9

♣K led

N
W   E
S

♠ A 10 3
♡ A 6 2
◇ A K 10 9 7 6 3
♣ —

West leads the king of clubs against South's contract of five diamonds.

How should declarer plan the play (assuming that the trumps
break 2–1)?

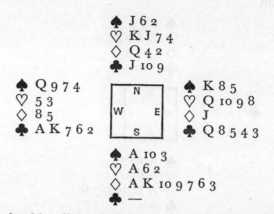

♠ J 6 2
♡ K J 7 4
◇ Q 4 2
♣ J 10 9

♠ Q 9 7 4
♡ 5 3
◇ 8 5
♣ A K 7 6 2

♠ K 8 5
♡ Q 10 9 8
◇ J
♣ Q 8 5 4 3

♠ A 10 3
♡ A 6 2
◇ A K 10 9 7 6 3
♣ —

Declarer should ruff the opening lead with ◇6, cash the ◇A and enter dummy with the ◇Q—still retaining the ◇3 in his own hand. A second club is ruffed high and followed by ♡ A K. Dummy's last club is led and South discards his losing heart. Regardless of the distribution, it is now impossible for the defence to avoid establishing either a heart or a second spade trick for declarer, or concede a ruff and discard.

Rubber bridge
North–South vulnerable
Dealer West

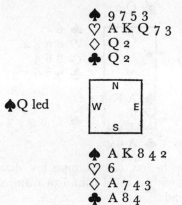

♠ 9 7 5 3
♡ A K Q 7 3
◇ Q 2
♣ Q 2

♠Q led

♠ A K 8 4 2
♡ 6
◇ A 7 4 3
♣ A 8 4

After West has opened the bidding with a weak no trump South arrives in six spades. West leads the queen of spades. South wins and cashes the ace of spades but East signals the bad news when he discards the three of clubs.

How should South plan the play?

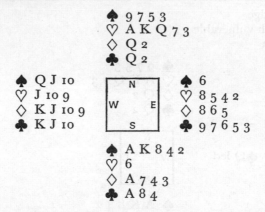

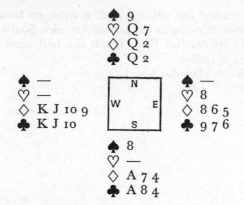

South must cash *two* top hearts, discarding a low diamond, ruff a heart in hand and exit with a third round of trumps. This is the position with West to lead:

Whichever minor suit West plays declarer must come to the balance of the tricks. The mistake to avoid is cashing off a third top heart, which squeezes the South hand; West can get off play with the minor suit which declarer has reduced to a doubleton. This will leave declarer with two losers in the other minor, only one of which can be discarded on dummy's long heart.

Rubber bridge
Game all
Dealer West

```
                        ♠ J 9 7
                        ♡ Q J 9 8 4
                        ◇ —
                        ♣ A 10 9 7 5


        ♠K led      ┌──────────┐
                    │    N     │
                    │ W      E │
                    │    S     │
                    └──────────┘


                        ♠ —
                        ♡ A 2
                        ◇ A K Q J 10 9 5 3
                        ♣ J 8 6
```

Bidding:

SOUTH	WEST	NORTH	EAST
	1♠	Pass	Pass
2♠	3♣	5♡	Pass
6◇	Pass	Pass	Pass

West leads the king of spades against South's contract of six diamonds. Having ruffed the spade in hand, South draws the trumps in three rounds, East holding three trumps and West two.

How should he continue?

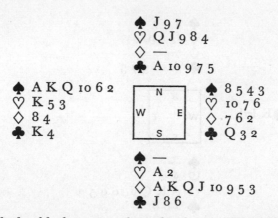

```
                    ♠ J 9 7
                    ♡ Q J 9 8 4
                    ◇ —
                    ♣ A 10 9 7 5

♠ A K Q 10 6 2    ┌─────────┐    ♠ 8 5 4 3
♡ K 5 3           │    N    │    ♡ 10 7 6
◇ 8 4             │ W     E │    ◇ 7 6 2
♣ K 4             │    S    │    ♣ Q 3 2
                  └─────────┘
                    ♠ —
                    ♡ A 2
                    ◇ A K Q J 10 9 5 3
                    ♣ J 8 6
```

South should play ace and another heart. ♡K is likely to be with West, but even if it isn't the 3–3 break or the ♡10 coming down will suffice.

This hand was played in a high-stake rubber game in London. The declarer, a ranking player, was mesmerized by the club intermediates and, having drawn trumps, led ♣6—an innocuous-looking card! West was wide awake however, and rose with ♣K, leaving declarer with insoluble entry problems.

Rubber bridge
Game all
Dealer South

♠ 5 2
♡ A J 10 6 5
♢ 7 5 3
♣ A 9 4

◇2 led

```
    N
W       E
    S
```

♠ A K 6 4
♡ 4 2
♢ A K 6 4
♣ K 8 7

Bidding:

SOUTH	WEST	NORTH	EAST
1 ♠	Pass	2 ♡	Pass
2 NT	Pass	3 NT	Pass
Pass	Pass		

West leads the two of diamonds against South's contract of three no trumps. East plays the nine on the first trick.

How should South plan the play?

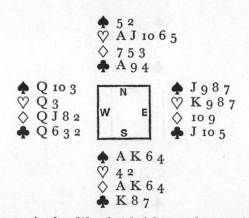

♠ 5 2
♡ A J 10 6 5
◇ 7 5 3
♣ A 9 4

♠ Q 10 3
♡ Q 3
◇ Q J 8 2
♣ Q 6 3 2

♠ J 9 8 7
♡ K 9 8 7
◇ 10 9
♣ J 10 5

♠ A K 6 4
♡ 4 2
◇ A K 6 4
♣ K 8 7

It is almost certain that West has led from a four-card diamond suit (from ◇ Q J 10 8 2 he would hardly lead the 2), so declarer should win the first trick and immediately direct his mind to the play of the heart suit. His problem is to establish three tricks in the suit and be able to enjoy them. If the hearts are 3–3 any reasonable method will suffice, but if they break 4–2 South's approach will have to be the correct one if he is to succeed. A heart should be led towards the dummy, and no matter what heart West plays dummy must play low. On regaining the lead declarer plays a second heart towards dummy, this time going up with ♡A. When both opponents follow and one honour card has appeared the rest is simple.

Note the result if South makes the mistake of running ♡10 at trick two. East, if he is wide awake, will duck, and now there is no way in which declarer can both establish and enjoy his third heart trick. Alternatively, West may go in with ♡Q on the first round, but declarer must resist the temptation to play dummy's ♡A.

Pairs
Game all
Dealer East

```
              ♠ Q 9
              ♡ A K 6 5
              ◇ A 7 4 2
              ♣ 9 8 6

        ♡3 led    ┌─────────┐
                  │    N    │
                  │ W     E │
                  │    S    │
                  └─────────┘

              ♠ K 10 8 5 2
              ♡ 10 2
              ◇ K Q 8
              ♣ K 5 2
```

Bidding:

SOUTH	WEST	NORTH	EAST
			1 ♡
1 ♠	2 ♣	3 ♠	Pass
Pass	Pass		

West leads the three of hearts against South's strange contract of three spades. Dummy wins, South following with the ten. The nine of spades is allowed to win the second trick and the next two tricks go to East's ace of spades and queen of clubs. East now switches to the nine of diamonds, which is won by South. The king of spades comes next, West discarding a club.

How should declarer plan the remainder of the play?

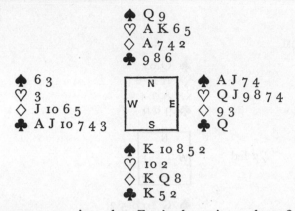

South must appreciate that East's shape is surely 4–6–2–1, and therefore to succeed in his contract he must arrange for East to squeeze his partner! At trick seven South must cash a second top diamond from his own hand and then exit with a spade to East's ♠J. This will be the position, East–West having taken three tricks and declarer five:

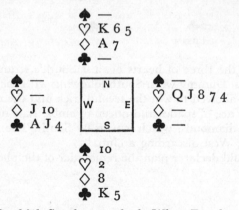

East leads ♡Q which South must duck. When East has to continue the suit ♡K wins while South discards the ♣5. Now a heart is ruffed in hand. Meanwhile West has been able to throw two clubs, but on the third heart he is squeezed remorselessly in the minor suits.

This hand occurred in a qualifying round of the Two Stars Championship at the Eastbourne Congress as long ago as 1950. The famous twins Bob and Jim Sharples were North–South: it was Jim who found the imaginative bid of 3♠ and Bob who played the hand so adroitly to land the contract.

Rubber bridge
Game all
Dealer East

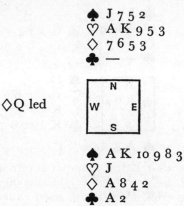

♠ J 7 5 2
♡ A K 9 5 3
◇ 7 6 5 3
♣ —

◇Q led

♠ A K 10 9 8 3
♡ J
◇ A 8 4 2
♣ A 2

West leads the queen of diamonds against South's contract of six spades. East follows with the king and South with the ace. The ace of spades is cashed, East playing the queen. The jack of hearts comes next and is covered by West's queen. A heart is ruffed in hand, East and West both following with small cards.

How should declarer plan the remainder of the play?

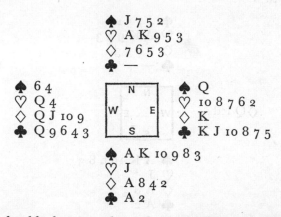

```
                  ♠ J 7 5 2
                  ♡ A K 9 5 3
                  ◇ 7 6 5 3
                  ♣ —
   ♠ 6 4                          ♠ Q
   ♡ Q 4          ┌─────────┐     ♡ 10 8 7 6 2
   ◇ Q J 10 9     │ N       │     ◇ K
   ♣ Q 9 6 4 3    │ W     E │     ♣ K J 10 8 7 5
                  │    S    │
                  └─────────┘
                  ♠ A K 10 9 8 3
                  ♡ J
                  ◇ A 8 4 2
                  ♣ A 2
```

Declarer should play a spade to dummy's ♠J and ruff a second heart. When West shows out he must cash ♣A, throwing a diamond from dummy, and ruff a club. Now ♡K is followed by dummy's last heart leaving East on play—South having discarded two diamonds. East must concede a ruff and discard at this point enabling South to fulfil his contract.

When this hand occurred at the table South made his contract in an elegant fashion, but his play incorporated an unnecessary risk. After one heart ruff declarer cashed ♣A and ruffed a club. Now he drew the last trump, remaining in dummy with ♠J, and played ♡5. When East played the ♡7 he threw a diamond, leaving East the choice of conceding a ruff and discard or leading up to dummy's heart tenace. The flaw with this plan was that West might well have held a third heart, in which case the contract would have failed.

Pairs
North–South vulnerable
Dealer East

♠ Q J 10
♡ A K 5 3
◇ K
♣ Q 10 9 5 2

◇2 led

```
      N
  W       E
      S
```

♠ A 7 3
♡ 10 8 7 6 4
◇ 5 3
♣ A 8 7

Bidding:

SOUTH	WEST	NORTH	EAST
			Pass
Pass	Pass	1♣	2◇
2♡	Pass	4♡	Pass
Pass	Pass		

West leads the two of diamonds against South's contract of four
hearts. East wins with the ace and switches to the two of spades
which declarer runs successfully to dummy's ten. On the ace of
hearts East follows with the jack and West with the two. Declarer
plays the queen of spades, which holds, and a third spade to his ace,
East contributing the four and six.

How should declarer proceed?

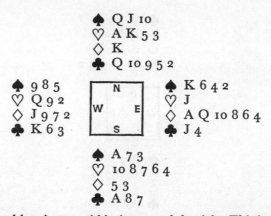

Declarer's problem is to avoid losing two club tricks. This is achieved by the technique of partial elimination. Declarer ruffs his last diamond in dummy and leads ♣Q. If this is covered his problems are over. If West wins and returns a club, again there is no problem. Finally, if West plays ♡9, declarer runs it, and either loses no trump trick or succeeds in endplaying East, whose distribution—if he turns up with ♡Q—must have been 4–2–6–1.

This hand occurred in the 1962 World Pairs Olympiad held in Cannes. South was Boris Schapiro, who skilfully avoided the club guess in the manner described. Not all the declarers 'guessed' so well, thus Schapiro and his partner, Terence Reese, emerged with a fine score on the hand.

Pairs
Love all
Dealer North

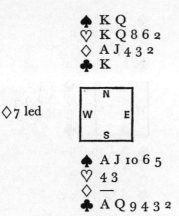

♠ K Q
♡ K Q 8 6 2
◊ A J 4 3 2
♣ K

◊ 7 led

♠ A J 10 6 5
♡ 4 3
◊ —
♣ A Q 9 4 3 2

With no opposition bidding North–South arrive in six spades. West leads the seven of diamonds.

How should South plan the play?

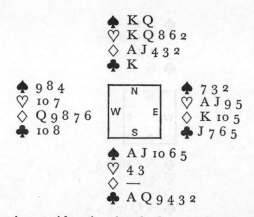

South's main consideration is whether spades or clubs are more likely to divide favourably. On the surface there appears to be nothing in it. Declarer cannot stand a bad break in both black suits, no matter how he plays. Equally, he can hardly go wrong if they both break well. The choice then appears to rest on no more than the toss of a coin—except for one fact. This is a match-pointed pairs contest and unquestionably some pairs are going to finish in 6 NT. In their case there will be no option: they will be forced to assume that the clubs divide 3–3, otherwise there will be no hope. In 6♠ South must assume the exact opposite—that spades divide 3–3 and clubs 4–2—so that he can profit over all the 6 NT bidders.

Once the correct assumption has been made the play itself is straightforward. The ♢A is followed by ♣K and a diamond ruff. A small club is ruffed in dummy and the last spade overtaken by the ace to draw the remainder of the trumps. South's hand is now high except for a losing heart.

The American Master Peter Rank recovered the ground he had 'lost' in the bidding with his accurate play on this deal from the Life Master Pairs at the Summer Nationals in Denver 1966.

Rubber bridge
East–West vulnerable
Dealer South

```
                        ♠ 10 7
                        ♡ 6 4 3
                        ◇ A 8 7 5
                        ♣ A Q 9 5

                      ┌─────────┐
                      │    N    │
        ♠6 led        │ W     E │
                      │    S    │
                      └─────────┘

                        ♠ J 4 3
                        ♡ A K
                        ◇ K Q 6 3
                        ♣ K 8 3 2
```

Bidding:

SOUTH	WEST	NORTH	EAST
1 ◇	Pass	2 ♣	Pass
2 NT	Pass	3 NT	Pass
Pass	Pass		

West leads the six of spades against South's contract of three no trumps. East takes the king and queen and then switches to the queen of hearts. Winning the heart trick perforce South cashes the king and queen of diamonds, but East shows out on the second diamond.

How should South play to make sure of his contract, on the reasonable assumption that the spades are divided 6–2?

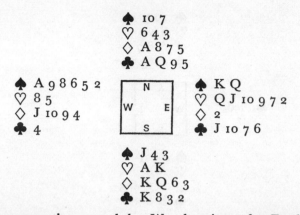

```
                    ♠ 10 7
                    ♡ 6 4 3
                    ◇ A 8 7 5
                    ♣ A Q 9 5
  ♠ A 9 8 6 5 2    ┌─────────┐    ♠ K Q
  ♡ 8 5           │    N    │    ♡ Q J 10 9 7 2
  ◇ J 10 9 4      │ W     E │    ◇ 2
  ♣ 4             │    S    │    ♣ J 10 7 6
                  └─────────┘
                    ♠ J 4 3
                    ♡ A K
                    ◇ K Q 6 3
                    ♣ K 8 3 2
```

We have correctly assumed that West has six spades. Furthermore, he holds four diamonds and at least one heart. It only remains to discover the club distribution. If he has two clubs the suit will break. On the other hand if he has a doubleton heart then he can hold no more than one club. So South must cash his second heart and when West follows a club is played to dummy's ♣A and the count is complete: East is known to hold ♣ J 10 7 6. The ◇A is cashed, extracting a reluctant heart from East, who is then thrown on lead with dummy's last heart. After making his two heart tricks he has to play a club, and his 'sure trick' disappears into thin air.

Rubber bridge
Love all
Dealer North

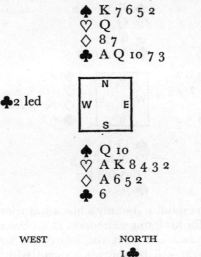

♠ K 7 6 5 2
♡ Q
♢ 8 7
♣ A Q 10 7 3

♣ 2 led

♠ Q 10
♡ A K 8 4 3 2
♢ A 6 5 2
♣ 6

Bidding:

SOUTH	WEST	NORTH	EAST
		1♣	3♢
4♡	Double	Pass	Pass
Pass			

West leads the two of clubs against South's contract of four hearts
doubled. Dummy's queen wins and a small spade is played to the
ten. West wins with the ace and plays the king of clubs.

How should declarer plan the play?

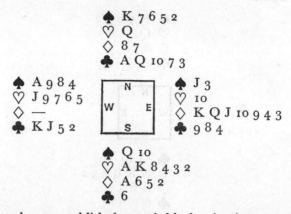

♠ K 7 6 5 2
♡ Q
◇ 8 7
♣ A Q 10 7 3

♠ A 9 8 4   ♠ J 3
♡ J 9 7 6 5   ♡ 10
◇ —   ◇ K Q J 10 9 4 3
♣ K J 5 2   ♣ 9 8 4

♠ Q 10
♡ A K 8 4 3 2
◇ A 6 5 2
♣ 6

South must plan to establish dummy's black-suit winners so that he has three discards for his losing diamonds. It is obvious that West is void in diamonds and also that the hearts are stacked. At the crucial moment West will be thrown on lead with a trump, but declarer must be careful to get rid of ♡8 so that he cannot be end-played by West!

The ♣K should be ruffed in hand, the ♠Q cashed, a trump played to dummy's ♡Q and a spade ruffed with ♡8. The ♡A and ◇A follow. If West ruffs—it only delays the issue if he discards—he can now exit with a trump, but South wins and throws the lead to West with his small heart. Dummy takes the last three tricks.

When this hand was played the declarer was Kenneth Konstam, a former world champion, and West was John Pugh, the British international. Konstam played the hand card-perfectly up to the time he ruffed a spade in his own hand—but then he ruffed with the ♡4 instead of ♡8. Spotting his only chance Pugh ruffed ◇A with the ♡J (having been careful to contribute ♡9 on ♡A), and subsequently was able to force the lead back to declarer. In the process he had to squander one trump trick, but his partner gained fair compensation with his diamond winners.

Rubber bridge
North–South vulnerable
Dealer East

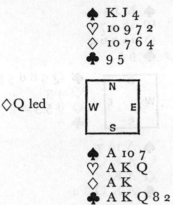

♠ K J 4
♡ 10 9 7 2
◇ 10 7 6 4
♣ 9 5

◇ Q led

♠ A 10 7
♡ A K Q
◇ A K
♣ A K Q 8 2

South arrives in six no trumps after East has opened the bidding with three spades. West leads the queen of diamonds, East following with the three. South cashes the ace of clubs and three rounds of hearts. East discards a spade on the ace of clubs and on the third round of hearts he again shows out, discarding a second low spade.

How should South continue?

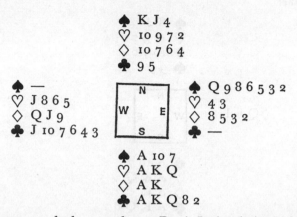

```
                    ♠ K J 4
                    ♡ 10 9 7 2
                    ◇ 10 7 6 4
                    ♣ 9 5
  ♠ —                              ♠ Q 9 8 6 5 3 2
  ♡ J 8 6 5         ┌─────────┐    ♡ 4 3
  ◇ Q J 9           │   N     │    ◇ 8 5 3 2
  ♣ J 10 7 6 4 3    │ W   E   │    ♣ —
                    │   S     │
                    └─────────┘
                    ♠ A 10 7
                    ♡ A K Q
                    ◇ A K
                    ♣ A K Q 8 2
```

Declarer must duck a spade to East! It is obvious that West holds the key to the remaining suits, and in order to bring pressure on him the spade suit must be played out. However, it is not good enough to pick up East's ♠Q, for that would sever the link with dummy and leave West with easy discards. Having taken his ♠Q, let's assume that East returns a spade, which South wins with ♠A, West discarding two clubs. South now cashes the ◇A and plays a spade to dummy's ♠K. This completes the triple squeeze on West.

This hand has an amusing history. Declarer was a modest performer who would have been totally incapable of the difficult play described above. At trick six she led a spade and inadvertently touched dummy's ♠J. East, reared in the traditions of Mrs Battle, insisted that the ♠J be played. The dénouement, as West was inexorably squeezed, was a sweet experience for Portia and just retribution for Shylock!

Teams
Game all
Dealer West

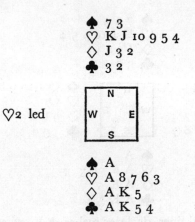

♠ 7 3
♡ K J 10 9 5 4
♢ J 3 2
♣ 3 2

♡2 led

♠ A
♡ A 8 7 6 3
♢ A K 5
♣ A K 5 4

West leads the two of hearts against South's contract of seven hearts, East contributing the queen.

How should declarer plan the play, and in what circumstances will he succeed?

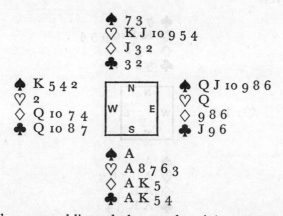

Playing along normal lines, declarer cashes ♠A, crosses to dummy and ruffs a spade. He now runs the hearts to arrive at this position, North to lead:

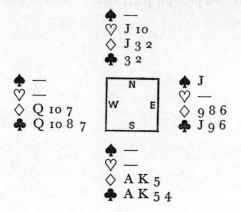

On ♡J South discards ◇5 and West . . .? If he discards a diamond ◇A and ◇K are cashed and dummy is re-entered with a club ruff, while if he parts with a club South's long club is established for the thirteenth trick.

This was the hand which virtually sealed the fate of the 1967–8 Silver Cup, the competition for those eliminated at the quarter- and semi-final stages of the Gold Cup. The winning team played quietly in six hearts while their opponents, the Scottish champions, bid to seven hearts. In practice South took the inferior line of the simple Vienna Coup, arriving at this ending:

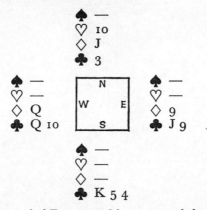

When the ♡10 was led East was able to control the club suit and the squeeze failed.

It is worth noting that the simple squeeze requires the hand with the guarded ◇Q to hold *five* clubs initially (26%), whereas the ruffing squeeze succeeds whenever the same hand holds four or more clubs and ◇Q (47%).

DEFENCE

Rubber bridge
East–West vulnerable
Dealer East

<pre>
                      ♠ K 5 3 2
                      ♡ 10 7 4
                      ◇ A Q 7
                      ♣ 6 4 2
     ♠ A Q 7 6   ┌─────────┐
     ♡ J 3 2   │   N   │
     ◇ 8 6 4 2   │ W   E │
     ♣ 9 3   │   S   │
                    └─────────┘
</pre>

Bidding:

SOUTH	WEST	NORTH	EAST
			1♠
3♡	3♠	4♡	Pass
Pass	Pass		

West decides to lead the nine of clubs against South's contract of four hearts. East wins with the jack and continues with the king and ace of clubs, South playing the five, seven and eight.

How should West plan the defence?

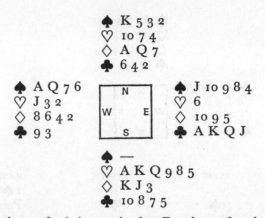

```
                    ♠ K 5 3 2
                    ♡ 10 7 4
                    ◇ A Q 7
                    ♣ 6 4 2
  ♠ A Q 7 6      ┌─────────┐      ♠ J 10 9 8 4
  ♡ J 3 2        │    N    │      ♡ 6
  ◇ 8 6 4 2      │ W     E │      ◇ 10 9 5
  ♣ 9 3          │    S    │      ♣ A K Q J
                 └─────────┘
                    ♠ —
                    ♡ A K Q 9 8 5
                    ◇ K J 3
                    ♣ 10 8 7 5
```

From the play so far it is certain that East has a fourth club and if West can persuade him to lead it the contract will be defeated. The big danger is that East will switch to a spade in an effort to cash West's ♠A, which is of course uncashable. How then should West deflect him from the wrong course?

Howard Schenken, the famous American Master, defended this hand in the Cavendish Club, New York. His partner was a player of modest ability, and Schenken decided that this was no time for half-measures. At trick three he made the spectacular discard of ♠A! With the ♠K clearly visible in the dummy East had really no option but to continue with a hesitant ♣Q. His puzzled frown gave way to enthusiastic praise when he appreciated the skill of his partner's discard.

Teams
East–West vulnerable
Dealer West

```
                    ♠ Q 9 8 7 4 2
                    ♡ 4
                    ◇ A
                    ♣ K 10 8 4 3
     ♠ J 5 3          ┌─────────┐
     ♡ A Q 9          │    N    │
     ◇ J 6 2          │ W     E │
     ♣ A Q J 9        │    S    │
                      └─────────┘
```

Bidding:

SOUTH	WEST	NORTH	EAST
	1 NT	2♠	Pass
4♡	Pass	Pass	Pass

West leads the two of diamonds against South's contract of four
hearts. East follows with the three and South with the five. South
ruffs a club in hand and then ruffs a low diamond in dummy.
South returns to hand with a second club ruff and leads the jack of
hearts.

How should West plan the defence?

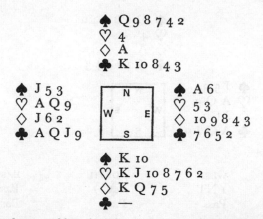

West's best chance of beating the contract is to find his partner with ♠A, in which case the defence can achieve a trump promotion. He should, therefore, win ♡Q and play his last diamond. When a second trump honour is led he takes his ♡A and leads a spade. The diamond return leaves South without resource.

This hand occurred in the final of the 1967–8 Gold Cup (Reese *v.* Gray). The contract was the same in both rooms and there was no swing on the board. In one room ♣A was led, giving South an easy ride. In the other room the play was projected to the position described in this problem, when West switched to a spade instead of continuing with a third diamond.

Rubber bridge
Love all
Dealer North

```
                        ♠ 8 2
                        ♡ Q J 9 2
                        ◇ Q 9 7 2
                        ♣ A Q 4
              ┌───────────────┐   ♠ 10 9 6 3
              │       N       │   ♡ A 5
  ◇3 led      │  W       E    │   ◇ A 10 8 5 4
              │       S       │   ♣ 6 5
              └───────────────┘
```

Bidding:

SOUTH	WEST	NORTH	EAST
		Pass	Pass
1♡	2♣	4♡	Pass
Pass	Pass		

West leads the three of diamonds against South's contract of four
hearts. East wins with the ace and returns the *four* of diamonds, in an
effort to prevent partner switching to a spade. South plays the king
of diamonds and West the four of trumps. Obediently West returns
the jack of clubs, dummy winning with the queen and South playing
the two. East wins the next trick with the ace of hearts, West following with the eight.

What card should East play now?

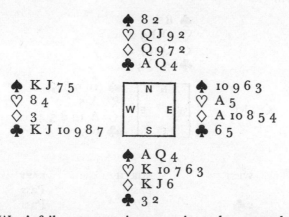

♠ 8 2
♡ Q J 9 2
◇ Q 9 7 2
♣ A Q 4

♠ K J 7 5   ♠ 10 9 6 3
♡ 8 4   ♡ A 5
◇ 3   ◇ A 10 8 5 4
♣ K J 10 9 8 7   ♣ 6 5

♠ A Q 4
♡ K 10 7 6 3
◇ K J 6
♣ 3 2

From West's failure to peter in trumps it can be assumed that he has no more, so East's thoughts should be directed to the end game. For declarer to succeed he will have to avoid losing a trick in the black suits, and unless he holds ♠K—which on the bidding is virtually impossible—the only way to achieve this end will be to squeeze West in spades and clubs. Therefore East must play a club now and break up the connecting link for the squeeze. The lesson that emerges is that the defence must attack the *irreplaceable* entry. If the long trump had been in the North hand the spade switch would have been correct.

When this hand occurred at rubber bridge Dick Cummings, the Australian international, appreciated the dangers of a spade switch. His play of ♣5 left declarer powerless. Observe what happens if he plays a spade. South will win, draw the last trump, cash the ◇J, enter dummy with a trump and cash ◇Q. Now he runs the remainder of the trumps and West will be squeezed into submission.

Teams
North–South vulnerable
Dealer West

```
                    ♠ A K Q 9 8 7
                    ♡ A 3
                    ◇ A 9 4 3
                    ♣ Q

                  ┌─────────┐      ♠ 3 2
                  │    N    │      ♡ 8 6
       ♣ J led    │ W     E │      ◇ Q 8 6 2
                  │    S    │      ♣ A K 8 6 5
                  └─────────┘
```

Bidding:

SOUTH	WEST	NORTH	EAST
	Pass	2♠	Pass
3◇	Pass	4◇	Pass
4♡	Pass	4 NT	Pass
5♣	Pass	6◇	Pass
Pass	Pass		

West leads the jack of clubs against South's contract of six diamonds, South following with the two.

Having won this trick how should East continue?

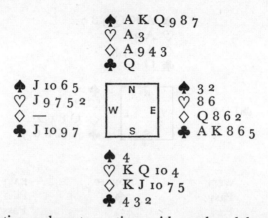

♠ A K Q 9 8 7
♡ A 3
◇ A 9 4 3
♣ Q

♠ J 10 6 5
♡ J 9 7 5 2
◇ —
♣ J 10 9 7

♠ 3 2
♡ 8 6
◇ Q 8 6 2
♣ A K 8 6 5

♠ 4
♡ K Q 10 4
◇ K J 10 7 5
♣ 4 3 2

It is tempting perhaps to continue with another club—and that is what happened at several tables during the 1969 B.B.L. Trials for the European Championships in Oslo. When East played this way South, hardly able to cope with four diamonds in the West hand, was *forced* into playing the trump suit correctly in order to make the contract. At one table East found the more imaginative switch to a spade. West co-operated by contributing ♠5, and declarer could scarcely be blamed for misplaying the trump suit.

Rubber bridge
Game all
Dealer North

```
                    ♠ 7 5 3
                    ♡ A K 7 2
                    ◇ 8 7 6
                    ♣ A Q J
              ┌─────────┐
              │    N    │   ♠ K 10 4
◇A led        │ W     E │   ♡ 10 9 6 5
              │    S    │   ◇ 9 4
              └─────────┘   ♣ K 9 8 4
```

Bidding:

SOUTH	WEST	NORTH	EAST
		1 ♣	Pass
4 ♠	Pass	Pass	Pass

West leads the two top diamonds against South's contract of four spades. On the second round South plays the queen. At trick three West continues with the jack of diamonds.

How should East plan the defence?

145

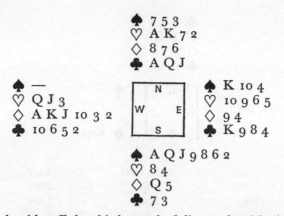

♠ 7 5 3
♡ A K 7 2
◇ 8 7 6
♣ A Q J

♠ —
♡ Q J 3
◇ A K J 10 3 2
♣ 10 6 5 2

♠ K 10 4
♡ 10 9 6 5
◇ 9 4
♣ K 9 8 4

♠ A Q J 9 8 6 2
♡ 8 4
◇ Q 5
♣ 7 3

East should ruff the third round of diamonds with ♠10, although this play will not immediately contribute anything to the defence. It should be obvious to East that South must hold all the missing trumps, and left to his own devices he will doubtless take the club finesse—which will lose—and the spade finesse—which will win. However, if East gives the impression of a man who is trying to promote a trump for partner, and in doing so reduces the outstanding trumps to just two, declarer may have second thoughts about the trump finesse.

East on this hand was Bobby Slavenburg, former World Pairs Champion, but on this occasion playing for hard cash rather than match points. Slavenburg earned his reward when the declarer laid down ♠A and after a few death wriggles had to admit defeat.

Rubber bridge
Love all
Dealer South

```
                      ♠ 7 4
                      ♡ 8 6
                      ♢ A 10 8 5 4 3
                      ♣ A 8 2

                   ┌─────────┐        ♠ 5
                   │    N    │        ♡ J 5 2
        ♢K led     │ W     E │        ♢ 9 7 2
                   │    S    │        ♣ J 9 6 5 4 3
                   └─────────┘
```

Bidding:

SOUTH	WEST	NORTH	EAST
2♡	2♠	3♢	Pass
4♡	Pass	5♣	Pass
6♡	Pass	Pass	Pass

West leads the king of diamonds against South's contract of six hearts. Declarer wins in dummy and then ruffs a diamond with the nine of hearts. At trick three he leads the ten of hearts, West following with the three.

How should East plan the defence?

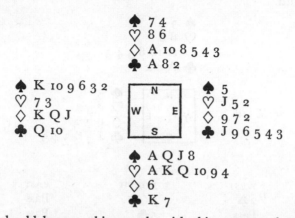

East should have nothing to do with this apparent bargain! It is obvious that declarer has conceived a machiavellian plot to create an entry in dummy. If East wins this trick nothing can stop declarer entering dummy with ♡8 to ruff a second diamond. Subsequently, after he has drawn trumps, dummy's ♣A provides the entry to the three winning diamonds and three spade discards.

When this hand occurred in a tough rubber bridge game in London East did in fact refuse ♡10. The declarer, a visiting American Life Master, drew trumps and played a cunning ♠J. This necessitated two good plays from West. First, he had to win this trick, otherwise two rounds of clubs would have followed and he would then have been thrown in with ◇Q to lead up to declarer's ♠ A Q. Secondly, he had to return a spade at once so as to disrupt the communications for the impending diamond–spade squeeze. Gruffly conceding defeat South remarked, 'Gee, you boys sure play a tough defence. It's harder to make a slam here than for a rich man to pass through the Pearly Gates.' Transatlantic concord was not entirely restored when East said, 'Never mind, you had 100 honours!'

Pairs
East–West vulnerable
Dealer South

```
                      ♠ 5
                      ♡ J 9 6
                      ◇ K Q 6 3 2
                      ♣ 6 5 4 2
                                      ♠ K 10 7 3 2
         ◇J led          N            ♡ Q 10 8
                    W        E        ◇ A 5 4
                         S            ♣ A 10
```

Bidding:

SOUTH	WEST	NORTH	EAST
1♠	Pass	1 NT	Pass
3♡	Pass	4♡	Pass
Pass	Pass		

West leads the jack of diamonds against South's contract of four hearts. East covers dummy's queen with the ace and South follows with the seven.

How should East plan the defence?

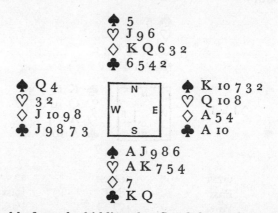

It is probable from the bidding that South has at least ten cards in the majors, so East must cash ♣A in case there is a discard coming on ◇K. When ♣A wins East can count three defensive tricks: one heart and two aces. As the celebrated Irish writer and player Jack Kelly appreciated, when defending this hand at the Killarney Congress, the setting trick must come from spades if it is to materialize at all. But unless East leads trumps declarer will no doubt be able to ruff his losers. Some players would be nervous of broaching trumps, as it might appear that they would be imperilling their sure trick. But provided East plays the ♡Q this is a case where fair exchange is better than no robbery. Kelly played ♡Q, and now South could ruff only two spades in the dummy; meanwhile East's trump trick became firmly established once more.

Rubber bridge
Love all
Dealer South

```
                    ♠ 8 2
                    ♡ 6 4
                    ◇ 7 5
                    ♣ A K J 7 6 5 4
  ♠ Q J 10 9 7 4    ┌──────────┐
  ♡ A J             │    N     │
  ◇ 10              │ W      E │
  ♣ Q 10 9 8        │    S     │
                    └──────────┘
```

Bidding:

SOUTH	WEST	NORTH	EAST
1 ♡	1 ♠	2 ♣	Pass
2 NT	Pass	3 NT	Pass
Pass	Pass		

West leads the queen of spades against South's contract of three no trumps. South wins with the ace and leads the three of clubs.

How should West plan the defence?

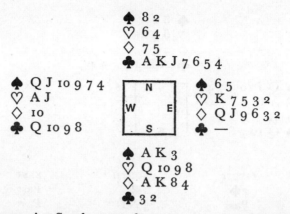

West must give South every chance to go wrong. It is obvious that much—probably everything—depends on the club suit. If South, as is likely on his rebid, has a doubleton, nothing can stop him making six tricks in the suit provided he plays correctly. But if West plays ♣Q at trick two South may fall into the trap and win this trick. Of course, declarer should play low from dummy automatically, but if he fails to do so West's opportunism will be rewarded.

Pairs
Love all
Dealer East

```
                        ♠ 9 8 7 5
                        ♡ K Q 6
                        ◇ 8 4
                        ♣ K Q 10 2
      ♠ 6 2                  ┌─────────┐
      ♡ 10 8 7 5 4 3 2       │    N    │
      ◇ 9 5 3               │ W     E │
      ♣ 3                    │    S    │
                            └─────────┘
```

Bidding:

SOUTH	WEST	NORTH	EAST
			2♣
2♠	Pass	4♠	5◇
5♠	Pass	Pass	Double
Pass	Pass	Pass	

West leads the three of clubs against South's contract of five spades doubled. Dummy plays the queen, East the ace and South the four. The jack of clubs is ruffed by West, South contributing the five, and the low heart return is won by East's ace, South following with the nine. East now plays the nine of clubs, South the eight, and West takes his second club ruff.

How should West continue the defence?

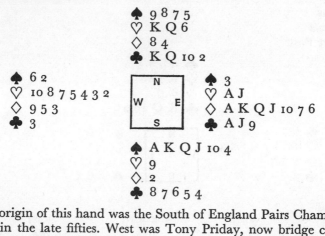

The origin of this hand was the South of England Pairs Championship in the late fifties. West was Tony Priday, now bridge corres-
pondent of the *Sunday Telegraph* and one of England's leading
players. His solution to the problem of what to play at trick five was
an all-important step on the road to eventual victory. If East has
eight diamonds and a singleton spade it would be fatal to play a
diamond. On the other hand, if East has seven diamonds and ♡J
it would be a mistake to play a heart. The defenders have taken
four tricks at this point and it is obvious that the fifth one will be
vital: 500 will ensure a better score than the reward for making a
non-vulnerable game. Indeed, it is now a question of *top* or *bottom*.

Although East's ♣9 looked rather like a second suit-preference
signal for a heart return, Priday reasoned that there was one piece
of irrefutable evidence which overshadowed everything else. If East
had wanted a heart ruff why had he not cashed the ♡A before
returning ♣J? This could only be wrong in the event of West's
holding eight hearts—an unlikely contingency. A further consideration was that if East had eight diamonds and only one heart, some
pairs would doubtless succeed in six diamonds, or at least push their
opponents to six spades. Priday returned a diamond, and earned a
rich reward for his logical thinking.

It is worth noting that declarer did not make West's decision any
easier by inserting a crafty ♣8 at trick four.

Teams
Game all
Dealer West

```
                    ♠ 8 3 2
                    ♡ 5 3 2
                    ◇ K 7
                    ♣ A Q J 10 8
```

◇3 led

```
        ┌─────────┐   ♠ 7 6 5
        │    N    │   ♡ 9 6
        │ W     E │   ◇ A Q 9 4
        │    S    │   ♣ 9 6 4 2
        └─────────┘
```

Bidding:

SOUTH	WEST	NORTH	EAST
	Pass	Pass	Pass
2♠	Pass	3♣	Pass
3♡	Pass	4♠	Pass
4 NT	Pass	5◇	Double
5♠	Pass	Pass	Pass

West leads the three of diamonds against South's contract of five spades. Dummy plays the seven, East the queen and South the eight. The ace of diamonds comes next, South contributing the jack and West the two.

How should East plan the defence?

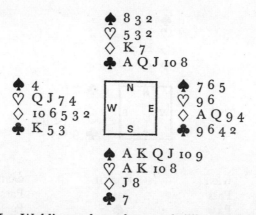

East was Jan Wohlin, perhaps the most brilliant player ever to have represented Sweden. At a critical stage in a match against a British touring team in the early fifties, Wohlin's defence on this hand drove the last nail into the British coffin. He returned ♣2 at trick three! With at least ten cards marked in the major suits South could hold at most one club, so Wohlin reasoned that the club switch could not cost. How right he was! Left with his communications intact, South would only have to run his trumps to exert irresistible pressure on West. On the last spade West would be unable to retain a heart guard and *three* clubs. With the communications severed West had an easy task. He had only to wait for the setting trick.

Rubber bridge
Love all
Dealer South

```
              ♠ J 9 7 6 4 3
              ♡ Q 3 2
              ◇ A 9
              ♣ 5 2
   ♠ 5              ┌─────────┐
   ♡ 9 8 7 6        │    N    │
   ◇ J 10 5 4 3 2   │ W     E │
   ♣ 8 7            │    S    │
                    └─────────┘
```

Bidding:

SOUTH	WEST	NORTH	EAST
2♣	Pass	3◇*	Pass
3♡	Pass	4♡	Pass
5♡	Pass	6♡	Pass
Pass	Pass		

   * Showing the ace of diamonds.

West leads the nine of hearts against South's contract of six hearts.
Declarer wins with the ten, East following suit. The ace of hearts
comes next, East discarding the eight of diamonds. The ace and
king of spades follow, East playing the two on the first round.

How should West plan the defence?

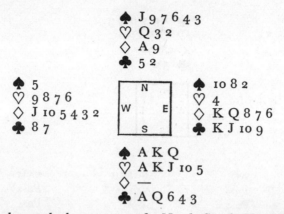

♠ J 9 7 6 4 3
♡ Q 3 2
◇ A 9
♣ 5 2

♠ 5
♡ 9 8 7 6
◇ J 10 5 4 3 2
♣ 8 7

♠ 10 8 2
♡ 4
◇ K Q 8 7 6
♣ K J 10 9

♠ A K Q
♡ A K J 10 5
◇ —
♣ A Q 6 4 3

Obviously not the best contract for North–South. Nevertheless, that will prove small solace unless West refuses to ruff the second round of spades. Furthermore, if South continues with ♠Q West must again refuse the Greek gift, even though he may never have another chance to make his small trump.

Canadian star Sammy Kehela was confronted with this problem in a rubber-bridge game in Toronto. Needless to say, he did not accept the lure that was dangled before him.

Rubber bridge
North–South vulnerable
Dealer North

<pre>
                        ♠ 6 4
                        ♡ A Q J 10
                        ◇ A Q 4
                        ♣ K Q J 7
  ♠ K Q 10 9 7 5   ┌─────────┐
  ♡ K 6   │   N   │
  ◇ 9 5   │ W   E │
  ♣ 6 4 2   │   S   │
                    └─────────┘
</pre>

Bidding:

SOUTH	WEST	NORTH	EAST
		1 ♡	Pass
1 NT	2♠	3 NT	Pass
Pass	Pass		

West leads the king of spades against South's contract of three no trumps. East follows with the two and South the three.

How good are West's chances of defeating the contract, and how should he plan the defence?

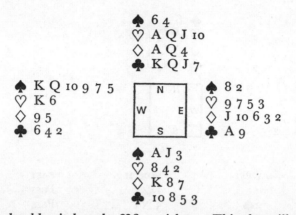

```
                    ♠ 6 4
                    ♡ A Q J 10
                    ◇ A Q 4
                    ♣ K Q J 7
  ♠ K Q 10 9 7 5      ┌─────────┐      ♠ 8 2
  ♡ K 6              │    N    │      ♡ 9 7 5 3
  ◇ 9 5             │ W     E │      ◇ J 10 6 3 2
  ♣ 6 4 2            │    S    │      ♣ A 9
                     └─────────┘
                    ♠ A J 3
                    ♡ 8 4 2
                    ◇ K 8 7
                    ♣ 10 8 5 3
```

West should switch to the ♡6 at trick two. This play will give him an excellent chance of defeating the contract. The layout of the spade suit is apparent. If East had held the ♠J he would have contributed it at trick one. If South had held four spades he would have preferred the bid of 1♠ to 1 NT. If South has ♣A there is surely nothing to be done since the contract is impregnable. But what if East has the ♣A? Put yourself in South's position and study the problem after a heart switch. Clearly South would be wrong to finesse if East has ♡K and West ♣A, since the defence will get their spade suit established before the clubs are cleared. But if South rises with ♡A and plays on clubs his contract is safe as long as West holds ♣A—regardless of who holds ♡K. Remembering the bidding it is not easy for South to make the winning play.

The setting for this hand was a high-standard game of rubber bridge in Switzerland. The contract failed after West found the killing heart switch at trick two.

Pairs
East–West vulnerable
Dealer South

```
                        ♠ Q 6 3
                        ♡ K Q 10 9 7 2
                        ◇ Q 8
                        ♣ A 3
                                        ♠ 10 5 2
           ◇K led    ┌─────────┐       ♡ 4
                     │    N    │       ◇ J 9 7 4
                     │ W     E │       ♣ 9 7 6 5 2
                     │    S    │
                     └─────────┘
```

Bidding:

SOUTH	WEST	NORTH	EAST
1♠	Double	Redouble	2♣
2♠	3♣	4♠	Pass
Pass	Pass		

West leads the king and ace of diamonds against South's contract of four spades. What plans should East make to guide the defence along the most hopeful lines?

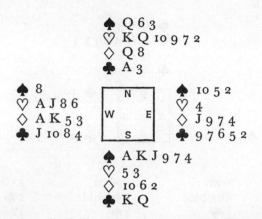

♠ Q 6 3
♡ K Q 10 9 7 2
◇ Q 8
♣ A 3

♠ 8
♡ A J 8 6
◇ A K 5 3
♣ J 10 8 4

♠ 10 5 2
♡ 4
◇ J 9 7 4
♣ 9 7 6 5 2

♠ A K J 9 7 4
♡ 5 3
◇ 10 6 2
♣ K Q

Two vital points should be clear to East. Left to himself West will surely switch to a club at trick three. Furthermore, with so many hearts in dummy, West, who probably has ♡A, will be afraid to play it unless suitably encouraged. Therefore, East should play the ◇7 or ◇9 on the first trick and follow it with the ◇J—a clear suit-preference signal asking for a heart switch.

This hand was played at a big national congress in the early sixties, and 4♠ succeeded at nearly every table. Where the defence followed the suggested lines West co-operated well and the declarer lost the first four tricks.

Pairs
North–South vulnerable
Dealer North

```
                    ♠ J 6 4 3
                    ♡ A Q 9 4
                    ◇ A K 8
                    ♣ Q 8

        ♠ A 8 5 2        ┌─────────┐
        ♡ J 10 2         │    N    │
        ◇ Q 3            │ W     E │
        ♣ A J 9 4        │    S    │
                         └─────────┘
```

Bidding:

SOUTH	WEST	NORTH	EAST
		1 ♠	Pass
1 NT	Pass	Pass	Pass

West decides to lead the jack of hearts against South's contract of one no trump. Declarer plays the ace from dummy, East contributing the three, and follows with three rounds of diamonds—East playing the seven, ten and jack. West discards the two of hearts on the third round of diamonds. East now switches to the seven of spades. Declarer plays the king and West wins with the ace.

How should West plan the defence and which card should he play next?

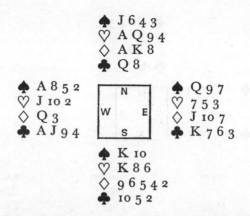

♠ J 6 4 3
♡ A Q 9 4
◇ A K 8
♣ Q 8

♠ A 8 5 2   ♠ Q 9 7
♡ J 10 2   ♡ 7 5 3
◇ Q 3   ◇ J 10 7
♣ A J 9 4   ♣ K 7 6 3

♠ K 10
♡ K 8 6
◇ 9 6 5 4 2
♣ 10 5 2

West should play ♣A at trick six—as the cards lie a small club works equally well—but in no circumstances must he play the ♠2. From the bidding and play so far it should be clear that South holds ♡K and therefore is unlikely to hold ♣K. On this basis West knows that he can take four club tricks. Having collected these tricks West will be on lead again. Now is the time to play a spade, and West must make his partner's life easy by playing the ♠8.

This is the type of hand that distinguishes the wolves from the lambs at the pairs game. West was the American expert Barry Crane, who has won the McKenney Trophy more often than any other player. This trophy is awarded to the winner of the most Master Points in the American tournament year. Here we see a good example of the qualities which have made him one of the leading exponents of the pairs game in the States.

At many tables West returned ♠2 at trick six and East, not unnaturally, put in ♠9. Declarer won with ♠10 and this gave him a total of no less than nine tricks—instead of six!

Rubber bridge
Game all
Dealer West

```
              ♠ J 9 8 3 2
              ♡ K 6 4
              ◇ Q 4
              ♣ K 9 3
   ♠ K 5          ┌─────────┐
   ♡ A 9 3        │    N    │
   ◇ K J 10 3     │ W     E │
   ♣ A J 8 2      │    S    │
                  └─────────┘
```

Bidding:

SOUTH	WEST	NORTH	EAST
	1 NT	Pass	Pass
2♡	Pass	3♡	Pass
4♡	Pass	Pass	Pass

West leads the ace and another heart against South's contract of four hearts. Declarer wins the second trick in hand, East following to both hearts. The ace and a small spade come next, East completing an echo. In with the king of spades West exits with a third heart, East throwing a small diamond. The king of hearts wins in dummy and South ruffs a spade and leads the four of clubs.

Are you satisfied with West's defence up to this point, and how should he continue?

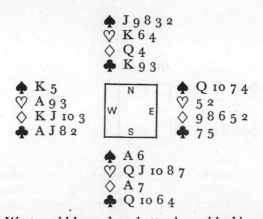

Of course West could have done better by unblocking ♠K, but all is not lost providing he denies declarer an extra entry to dummy as he tries to establish and enjoy his fifth spade. The ♣J on declarer's ♣4 does just that! Declarer may win with dummy's ♣K and ruff a spade. However, when he plays a club West can duck an honour or rise with ♣A on ♣6, which deprives declarer of the second vital entry. If West plays a low club on ♣4 instead of ♣J, dummy's ♣9 wins and a spade is ruffed with the last trump. Now a club to ♣K followed by the fifth spade, on which declarer throws a club, squeezes West in the minors: he will have to bare either the ◇K or the ♣A.

Rubber bridge
Love all
Dealer East

$\spadesuit$ K J 9 8 3
$\heartsuit$ A Q J 5
$\diamondsuit$ 10 4
$\clubsuit$ 8 3

$\spadesuit$ A 7 4
$\heartsuit$ K 8 6
$\diamondsuit$ K J 8 2
$\clubsuit$ Q 6 2

```
        N
    W       E
        S
```

Bidding:

SOUTH	WEST	NORTH	EAST
			Pass
1$\clubsuit$	Double	Redouble	2$\clubsuit$
Double	2$\diamondsuit$	2$\spadesuit$	3$\diamondsuit$
Pass	Pass	3$\heartsuit$	Pass
3 NT	Pass	Pass	Double
Pass	Pass	Pass	

A typical light-hearted rubber bridge auction with everyone in the bidding. West leads the two of diamonds and is a little disappointed to see dummy's ten holding the trick—East contributing the seven. Declarer plays the eight of clubs from dummy and runs it to West's queen.

How should West plan the defence?

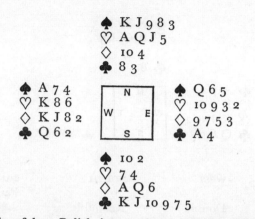

As the colourful ex-Polish international Michael Wolach demonstrated, West should play a diamond at trick three right into the A Q tenace! Although this sacrifices one trick immediately it totally eclipses the club suit, since the link to South's hand is severed beyond repair. It is true that East would have saved the day by going up with the ♣A and leading a diamond, but that would have been a suicidal move had declarer held a seven-card suit. As the play went West must assume that his partner holds the ♣A and ♠Q and disrupt the communications accordingly.

Pairs, Butler method of scoring
Love all
Dealer East

$\spadesuit$ A 10 7
$\heartsuit$ J 8 6 5 2
$\diamondsuit$ A 4
$\clubsuit$ K J 8

```
        N
      +-----+
$\diamondsuit$J led  | W  E |
      |  S  |
      +-----+
```

$\spadesuit$ 9
$\heartsuit$ K Q 10 3
$\diamondsuit$ K 8 7 6
$\clubsuit$ Q 9 5 2

Bidding:

SOUTH	WEST	NORTH	EAST
			Pass
3$\spadesuit$	Pass	4$\spadesuit$	Pass
Pass	Pass		

West leads the jack of diamonds against South's contract of four spades. East wins with the king, South following with the two.

How should East plan the defence, and which card should he play at trick two?

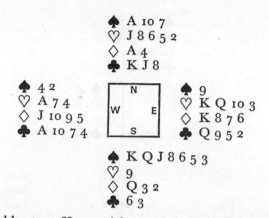

♠ A 10 7
♡ J 8 6 5 2
◇ A 4
♣ K J 8

♠ 4 2
♡ A 7 4
◇ J 10 9 5
♣ A 10 7 4

♠ 9
♡ K Q 10 3
◇ K 8 7 6
♣ Q 9 5 2

♠ K Q J 8 6 5 3
♡ 9
◇ Q 3 2
♣ 6 3

East should return ♡3 at trick two. It is likely that West has both the missing aces, but the defence will still require one more trick if the contract is to be defeated. There are three good reasons for playing precisely ♡3. First, West will have a shrewd idea how many hearts declarer holds and may be able to decide whether to try and cash a second heart or switch to a club. Secondly, when East plays a low heart declarer is more likely to misplace the club honours if he is forced to a guess. Thirdly, a top heart may leave the wrong defender on lead and enable declarer to set up the heart suit without ever having to make a guess in clubs.

When this hand occurred in the *Sunday Times* International Pairs Championship, 1970, East, the Portuguese international C. S. Teixeira, made the fine play of returning the ♡3. J. A. Debonnaire, his partner and also a Portuguese international, drew the right inference and returned a small club. Justice was served when declarer played dummy's ♣J.

Pairs
Game all
Dealer East

```
                        ♠ —
                        ♡ 9 6 5 4 3 2
                        ◊ 10 8 7 3
                        ♣ 6 3 2

                     ┌─────────┐          ♠ 8 5
                     │    N    │          ♡ K Q J 10
         ♠3 led      │ W     E │          ◊ A K Q J
                     │    S    │          ♣ K J 10
                     └─────────┘
```

Bidding:

SOUTH	WEST	NORTH	EAST
			2 NT
Double	Pass	3♡	Double
3 NT	Pass	Pass	Double
Pass	Pass	Pass	

West leads the three of spades (from a five-card suit) against South's contract of three no trumps doubled. South wins and cashes five more spade tricks.

How should East plan the defence to give himself the best chance of defeating the contract?

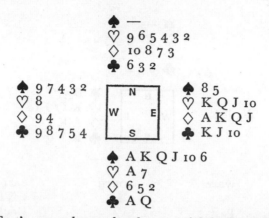

Despite East's power-house the chances of defeating 3 NT are very slim. Indeed, they only exist if South can be persuaded to misjudge the actual distribution. East should appreciate that there can be no point in retaining the guarded ♣K, for in that case he is sure to be thrown on lead to concede the last two club tricks. East is known to hold all the outstanding points, but if he discards the ♣ J 10, ♡J and ◇J, South will have to guess whether the falsecard is in hearts or clubs. No doubt the ♡A will be cashed before he finally makes a decision, but East will not help the declarer as he follows with ♡Q.

This hand occurred originally in the 1960 National Pairs Championship final, and in fact 3 NT was defeated on two occasions when East blanked ♣K early in the game. At one table Paul Spurway, the English international, was East. He showed excellent judgement when continuing with 4♣ over South's 3 NT—his brother, John, who was West, having bid 3♣ on the first round. Reluctant to accept the penalty, South pressed on to 4♠, which West doubled. The ♡8 was led, but South could not avoid the one trick set. Paul Spurway's inspired bid gave East–West a big score on the hand.

Teams
Game all
Dealer South

```
              ♠ 5 4
              ♡ J 7
              ◇ A Q J 8
              ♣ A 10 7 5 4
                         ♠ A 9
           ┌─────────┐   ♡ 5 3 2
           │    N    │   ◇ 3
  ♡K led   │ W     E │   ♣ K Q J 9 6 3 2
           │    S    │
           └─────────┘
```

Bidding:

SOUTH	WEST	NORTH	EAST
1♠	Pass	2♣	Pass
2♠	Pass	3◇	Pass
3 NT	Pass	Pass	Pass

West leads the king of hearts against South's contract of three no trumps. South wins the third round of hearts with the ace, dummy discarding a small club. The nine of diamonds is led to dummy's jack and a small spade played from the table. East contributes the nine, South the king and West the three.

How should East plan the defence?

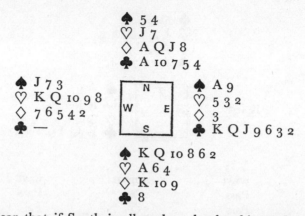

♠ 5 4
♡ J 7
♢ A Q J 8
♣ A 10 7 5 4

♠ J 7 3
♡ K Q 10 9 8
♢ 7 6 5 4 2
♣ —

♠ A 9
♡ 5 3 2
♢ 3
♣ K Q J 9 6 3 2

♠ K Q 10 8 6 2
♡ A 6 4
♢ K 10 9
♣ 8

It is clear that if South is allowed to develop his spades he will make his contract. It is also clear that, unless his spades are solid apart from the ♠A, which seems inconsistent with the play so far, he must re-enter dummy with a second diamond to play spades through East once again. Therefore East must plan to discard his ♠A on the second round of diamonds! Restricted to two tricks in spades, declarer will be incapable of making more than eight tricks in all.

Rubber bridge
Game all
Dealer South

♠ Q 8 3
♥ A J 10 9 8 4
♦ K 6
♣ 8 2

♠ 7 4
♥ K 5 2
♦ Q 9 8 5 4 2
♣ 5 4

◇J led

N
W   E
S

Bidding:

SOUTH	WEST	NORTH	EAST
1 ♣	Pass	1 ♡	Pass
1 ♠	Pass	3 ♡	Pass
4 NT	Pass	5 ◇	Pass
5 NT	Pass	6 ◇	Pass
6 NT	Pass	Pass	Pass

West leads the jack of diamonds against South's contract of six no trumps. Declarer wins in hand with the ace and plays the queen of hearts. East wins the second round of hearts, partner following twice.

Which suit should East play at trick four, and why?

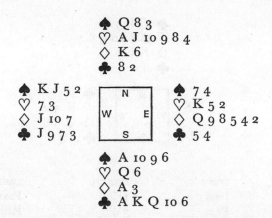

♠ Q 8 3
♡ A J 10 9 8 4
◇ K 6
♣ 8 2

♠ K J 5 2
♡ 7 3
◇ J 10 7
♣ J 9 7 3

♠ 7 4
♡ K 5 2
◇ Q 9 8 5 4 2
♣ 5 4

♠ A 10 9 6
♡ Q 6
◇ A 3
♣ A K Q 10 6

It is essential that East plays a diamond at trick four, which forces declarer to enjoy his heart winners *immediately*. Defending on these lines West discards after declarer and as long as he watches the discards with care he must make either a spade or a club trick.

When this hand was played East thought he ought to tackle one of the black suits and chose to play ♣5. South won, cashed his ♠A (Vienna Coup), entered dummy with the ◇K and ran down the hearts. West could not resist the pressure.

Rubber bridge
Game all
Dealer West

```
                        ♠ J 9 6
                        ♡ K
                        ◇ A K Q 9 6 4
                        ♣ 10 5 3
        ♠ K 2              ┌─────────┐
        ♡ A Q 6 5          │    N    │
        ◇ 10 7 3           │ W     E │
        ♣ J 9 6 2          │    S    │
                           └─────────┘
```

Bidding:

SOUTH	WEST	NORTH	EAST
	Pass	1 ◇	Pass
1 ♡	Pass	2 ◇	Pass
2 NT	Pass	3 NT	Pass
Pass	Pass		

West leads the two of clubs against South's contract of three no trumps. Dummy plays low and East's queen is taken by declarer's king. Declarer now plays a low heart towards the dummy.

How should West plan the defence?

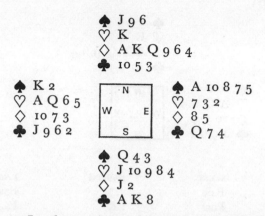

A few years ago London was invaded by those two brilliant Australian players Dick Cummings and Tim Seres. It was Seres who held the West hand in this deal. Quickly appreciating the probable lie of the cards, he won the second trick with ♡A and switched to the ♠2. East played his ♠A and returned a club to defeat the contract.

It was essential to have a club lead through declarer. West must assume that South does not have the ♠A, for if he had nine tricks would present no problem. In any case, it would appear that he has the ♣ A K and ♡J; with ♠A as well he would probably have tried 3 NT on the second round.

Rubber bridge
Game all
Dealer North

```
                    ♠ A 6 4 2
                    ♡ 8 5 4 2
                    ◇ A K Q 10 5
                    ♣ —
        ♠ Q 8 7 5        ┌─────────┐
        ♡ Q 10 6         │    N    │
        ◇ 8 3            │ W     E │
        ♣ K Q J 8        │    S    │
                         └─────────┘
```

Bidding:

SOUTH	WEST	NORTH	EAST
		1 ◇	Pass
1 ♠	Pass	3 ♣	Pass
4 ♠	Pass	Pass	Pass

West leads the king of clubs against South's contract of four spades. Dummy ruffs and plays a low spade to the jack, East following with the three.

How should West plan the defence?

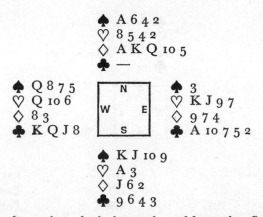

♠ A 6 4 2
♡ 8 5 4 2
◇ A K Q 10 5
♣ —

♠ Q 8 7 5
♡ Q 10 6
◇ 8 3
♣ K Q J 8

♠ 3
♡ K J 9 7
◇ 9 7 4
♣ A 10 7 5 2

♠ K J 10 9
♡ A 3
◇ J 6 2
♣ 9 6 4 3

West's best chance is to duck the spade and hope that South suffers from an *idée fixe*. If he should assume that the spade finesse is right he may go to dummy with the ♠A, with fatal effect. He can ruff one more club and try for discards on the diamonds. However, West will ruff the third round and cash two more clubs. Subsequently the defence must make a heart trick for one down.

Rubber bridge
Love all
Dealer South

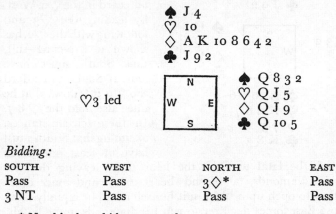

♠ J 4
♡ 10
◇ A K 10 8 6 4 2
♣ J 9 2

♡3 led

N
W E
S

♠ Q 8 3 2
♡ Q J 5
◇ Q J 9
♣ Q 10 5

Bidding:

SOUTH	WEST	NORTH	EAST
Pass	Pass	3◇*	Pass
3 NT	Pass	Pass	Pass

* North's three bids are sound.

West leads the three of hearts against South's contract of three no trumps. South takes East's jack with the king and—wisely—ducks a diamond to East, West following suit. East cashes the queen of hearts, South following with the nine and West with the two while dummy discards the two of clubs.

How should East continue the defence?

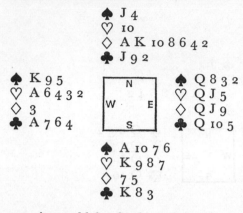

♠ J 4
♡ 10
◇ A K 10 8 6 4 2
♣ J 9 2

♠ K 9 5
♡ A 6 4 3 2
◇ 3
♣ A 7 6 4

♠ Q 8 3 2
♡ Q J 5
◇ Q J 9
♣ Q 10 5

♠ A 10 7 6
♡ K 9 8 7
◇ 7 5
♣ K 8 3

The first point that should strike East is that South has played a very foolish falsecard in the ♡9. West, by leading the ♡3 and following with the ♡2, has shown a five-card suit, thus South must have four. If South can afford the ♡9 it follows that he must also hold the ♡ 8 7. In these circumstances, assuming that South must have at least one black ace, it would be fatal to clear the heart suit, leaving declarer to cash six diamonds, a second heart trick and one black ace. For East to open up a black suit himself could be equally fatal. But suppose East forces declarer to run his diamonds immediately. . . . That will surely facilitate the defence and give declarer quite a problem.

With the lead in dummy and the last diamond still to cash this is the position:

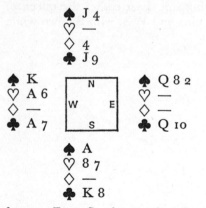

♠ J 4
♡ —
◇ 4
♣ J 9

♠ K
♡ A 6
◇ —
♣ A 7

♠ Q 8 2
♡ —
◇ —
♣ Q 10

♠ A
♡ 8 7
◇ —
♣ K 8

The ◇4 is led, which gives South his seventh trick. East parts with the ♠2 but South is in trouble. In fact he cannot make a safe discard. Meanwhile West hovers like a bird of prey poised for the kill!

This hand occurred in a modest game of family bridge and, not surprisingly, when South followed with the ♡9 at trick three the significance of this stupid falsecard was lost on East. So she continued with the ♡5 . . . at least, that was the intention, but to her horror she saw that she had dropped the ◇J on the table! 'Oh, partner, I am so sorry. I have pulled the wrong card and given them the contract,' she cried in anguish. When the contract was defeated by one trick, East innocently repeated her plea for forgiveness. 'Of course we would have beaten it by more had I not pulled the wrong card.'

Teams
North–South vulnerable
Dealer North

                              ♠ Q 10 5
                              ♡ Q 10 8 3
                              ◇ A 6 2
                              ♣ Q 10 4

    ♠ 7 4 3 2   ┌─────────┐
    ♡ 6 5   │   N   │
    ◇ K J 8 7 3   │ W   E │
    ♣ K 7   │   S   │
                       └─────────┘

Bidding :

SOUTH	WEST	NORTH	EAST
		Pass	Pass
2 NT	Pass	4 ♣*	Pass
4 NT†	Pass	6 NT	Pass
Pass	Pass		

    * Gerber, asking for aces.
    † Three aces.

West leads a spade against South's contract of six no trumps.
Declarer cashes four rounds of spades, dummy discarding the two of
diamonds and East the two of clubs and four of diamonds. South
now cashes the ace of clubs followed by four rounds of hearts.

How should West plan the defence?

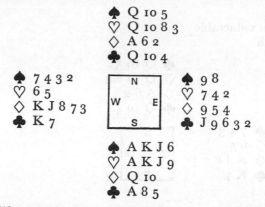

♠ Q 10 5
♡ Q 10 8 3
◇ A 6 2
♣ Q 10 4

♠ 7 4 3 2
♡ 6 5
◇ K J 8 7 3
♣ K 7

♠ 9 8
♡ 7 4 2
◇ 9 5 4
♣ J 9 6 3 2

♠ A K J 6
♡ A K J 9
◇ Q 10
♣ A 8 5

Perhaps West was lucky to have been given two additional chances of disembarrassing himself of the ♣K. When declarer cashed the ♣A he practically made a public announcement that he did not hold the ♣J. It follows that East must have this card, and West should let him assume control of the suit by throwing his king. If West defends like this declarer will have to lose two tricks in the minors; but if West still holds ♣K he will be thrown in at trick ten and will then have to concede an extra diamond trick to declarer's ◇Q.

This hand occurred in the 1969 World Championships in Rio de Janeiro, Italy *v.* China. In one room Avarelli (North) and Belladonna (South) reached the slightly superior contract of 6♡, played by Belladonna. Against this contract the defence, Tai (East) and P. Huang (West), for China, were helpless. Had West parted with the ♣K Belladonna would have discarded a club from dummy—losing just one diamond.

In the other room China were represented by F. Huang (North) and C. E. Shen (South), while D'Alelio (East) and Pabis-Ticci (West) held the fort for Italy. Against 6 NT the play went as described, and Pabis-Ticci had a great opportunity to make the headlines, especially when the declarer played a third and a fourth heart. To be fair, these situations are always a little more comfortable away from the table, and eventually Shen executed the same throw-in play that Belladonna had enjoyed in his room . . . so there was no swing on the board.

Teams
Game all
Dealer South

```
                          ♠ 9 7 4
                          ♡ 8 3
                          ◇ A Q 10 8 7 2
                          ♣ 7 5
        ♠ Q 10          ┌─────────────┐
        ♡ 10 9 6 4 2    │      N      │
        ◇ J 9 3         │  W       E  │
        ♣ Q J 6         │      S      │
                        └─────────────┘
```

Bidding:

SOUTH	WEST	NORTH	EAST
1 ♣	Pass	1 ◇	Pass
2 ♠	Pass	3 ◇	Pass
3 NT	Pass	Pass	Pass

West leads the four of hearts against South's contract of three no trumps. East plays the jack and South the ace. The five of diamonds is now led towards the dummy; West plays the three, dummy the ten and East the four. Declarer returns to hand with the ace of clubs and leads the six of diamonds.

How should West plan the defence?

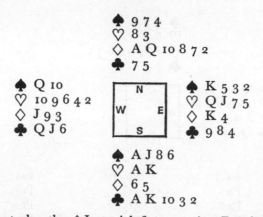

```
              ♠ 9 7 4
              ♡ 8 3
              ◇ A Q 10 8 7 2
              ♣ 7 5
♠ Q 10          ┌─────────┐    ♠ K 5 3 2
♡ 10 9 6 4 2    │    N    │    ♡ Q J 7 5
◇ J 9 3         │  W   E  │    ◇ K 4
♣ Q J 6         │    S    │    ♣ 9 8 4
                └─────────┘
              ♠ A J 8 6
              ♡ A K
              ◇ 6 5
              ♣ A K 10 3 2
```

West must play the ◇J at trick four, *not* ◇9. East has played well
by ducking the first round, but if West now contributes the ◇9
declarer will realize that he has no chance of bringing in the suit if
West started with ◇ K J 9 3. As a result he is sure to play the ◇A
from dummy intending to turn to clubs—at which point the roof
will fall in!

When this hand was played in a multiple team event the final
contract was invariably 3 NT. All the Easts who won the first round
of diamonds and played back a heart gave the declarers no further
headaches. Where the ◇K was held up but the ◇9 contributed by
West on the second round, North–South enjoyed a bonanza. Where
both defenders co-operated, declarer was limited to eight tricks.

It is worth noting that declarer should have ducked a club when
the ◇10 held. He would then be able to succeed where the clubs
are divided without reference to the diamonds.

Rubber bridge
Game all
Dealer East

```
                    ♠ J 7 5 4
                    ♡ 8 7 6
                    ◇ K Q
                    ♣ 10 8 3 2
                ┌─────────┐   ♠ K 2
                │    N    │   ♡ A 10 5
     ◇ 2 led    │ W     E │   ◇ A 10 7 6 5 3
                │    S    │   ♣ Q 4
                └─────────┘
```

Bidding:

SOUTH	WEST	NORTH	EAST
			1 ◇
Double	2 ◇	Pass	Pass
2 ♠	Pass	4 ♠	Pass
Pass	Pass		

West leads the two of diamonds against South's contract of four spades. East wins and switches to the five of hearts. South plays the king and West the three. South cashes the ace and king of clubs, West following with the nine and six, and exits with the nine of hearts, on which West completes a peter with the two.

How should East plan the defence?

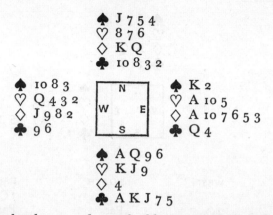

East must take the second round of hearts with the ♡A, not the
♡10. His plan should be to play a third heart which West will win
with the ♡Q. Now it will be West's turn to tighten the screw. A
fourth heart allows East to ruff with the ♠K and promote partner's
♠10 to winning rank.

When this hand occurred East was Kenneth Konstam. On the
second round of hearts Konstam considered the matter only briefly
before winning with ♡A and playing back ♡10. Unfortunately,
however, his partner had read somewhere that it was bad bridge to
concede a ruff and discard, and the diamond return spoilt what
would have been a most unusual defence.

Rubber bridge
North–South vulnerable
Dealer North

```
              ♠ J 9 8 7 5
              ♡ A 10 6
              ◇ A 6
              ♣ A 8 4
   ♠ K Q        ┌─────────┐
   ♡ 3 2        │    N    │
   ◇ J 9 5 3    │ W     E │
   ♣ J 9 7 5 2  │    S    │
                └─────────┘
```

Bidding:

SOUTH	WEST	NORTH	EAST
		1 ♠	Pass
3 NT	Pass	Pass	Pass

West leads the five of clubs against South's contract of three no trumps. Dummy plays low, East the queen and South the king. Declarer, proceeding on pedestrian lines, cashes three top hearts and three top diamonds. Having won the first seven tricks declarer then throws West on lead with the jack of diamonds, dummy having discarded two spades.

Playing with a partner who is not renowned for his powers of concentration, how should West proceed?

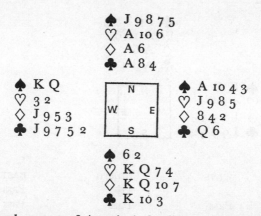

♠ J 9 8 7 5
♡ A 10 6
◇ A 6
♣ A 8 4

♠ K Q
♡ 3 2
◇ J 9 5 3
♣ J 9 7 5 2

♠ A 10 4 3
♡ J 9 8 5
◇ 8 4 2
♣ Q 6

♠ 6 2
♡ K Q 7 4
◇ K Q 10 7
♣ K 10 3

Robert Jordan, one of America's leading internationals, found a neat solution to this problem when playing rubber bridge at Crockford's Club, London. At trick nine he led the ♠Q! It was obvious that East held the ♠A and that he could play a club after winning the spade trick and cashing a master heart. There was no hitch in Jordan's plan, but as he entered plus 100 on the scoresheet his partner remarked in reproving tones, 'You know, partner, you misled me about your spade holding. I thought South held ♠K.'

Rubber bridge
Love all
Dealer East

```
                    ♠ Q 7 4
                    ♡ J 10 2
                    ◇ K 7
                    ♣ A K J 6 2

                   ┌─────────┐       ♠ J 9 8 2
                   │    N    │       ♡ K 8 5 4
        ♡3 led     │ W     E │       ◇ J 10 3
                   │    S    │       ♣ Q 8
                   └─────────┘
```

Bidding:

SOUTH	WEST	NORTH	EAST
			Pass
1 ♠	Pass	2 ♣	Pass
2 ◇	Pass	2 ♡	Pass
2 NT	Pass	3 NT	Pass
Pass	Pass		

West leads the three of hearts against South's contract of three no trumps. East wins with the king, South following with the nine, and returns the four. West wins this trick, South contributing the queen, and plays a third heart, which is won in dummy, South discarding the two of diamonds. The ace of clubs is cashed and a small spade played to declarer's ace. The club finesse now loses to East.

How should East plan the defence?

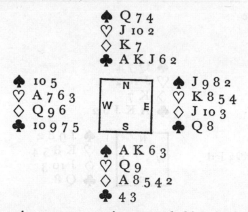

♠ Q 7 4
♡ J 10 2
◇ K 7
♣ A K J 6 2

♠ 10 5   ♠ J 9 8 2
♡ A 7 6 3   ♡ K 8 5 4
◇ Q 9 6   ◇ J 10 3
♣ 10 9 7 5   ♣ Q 8

♠ A K 6 3
♡ Q 9
◇ A 8 5 4 2
♣ 4 3

East must resist any temptation to cash his winning heart. That play would result in declarer's coming to nine tricks via a double squeeze. If East exits with either a diamond or a spade South has no play for his contract against best defence. If East should cash his heart winner this will be the three-card ending, dummy to play:

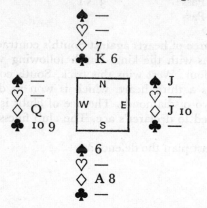

♠ —
♡ —
◇ 7
♣ K 6

♠ —   ♠ J
♡ —   ♡ —
◇ Q   ◇ J 10
♣ 10 9   ♣ —

♠ 6
♡ —
◇ A 8
♣ —

The ♣K is played and it is now East's turn to be squeezed, West having come under pressure when the spades were cashed.

Rubber bridge
North–South + 60
Dealer North

```
                    ♠ A 10 9 6
                    ♡ J 6
                    ◇ A
                    ♣ A K J 8 4 2
                         ┌─────────┐        ♠ 8 7 3 2
                         │    N    │        ♡ K 9 4
          ◇J led         │ W     E │        ◇ K Q 6 4 3 2
                         │    S    │        ♣ —
                         └─────────┘
```

Bidding:

SOUTH	WEST	NORTH	EAST
		1♣	Pass
1♡	Pass	1♠	Pass
2♡	Pass	3♡	Pass
4♡	Pass	5 NT*	Pass
6♡†	Pass	Pass	Pass

* Grand Slam Force.

† North–South are playing step responses, thus 6♡ shows two of the top three honours.

West leads the jack of diamonds against South's contract of six hearts. At trick two declarer plays the six of hearts from dummy. How should East plan the defence?

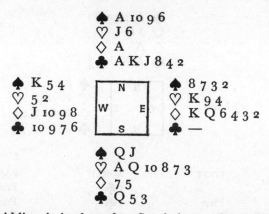

♠ A 10 9 6
♡ J 6
◇ A
♣ A K J 8 4 2

♠ K 5 4
♡ 5 2
◇ J 10 9 8
♣ 10 9 7 6

♠ 8 7 3 2
♡ K 9 4
◇ K Q 6 4 3 2
♣ —

♠ Q J
♡ A Q 10 8 7 3
◇ 7 5
♣ Q 5 3

From the bidding it is clear that South has a six-card heart suit headed by the A Q. Furthermore, East knows that any black-suit finesse is sure to succeed. The only hope seems to lie in diverting South from his probable intention of ruffing a diamond in dummy. East was Benito Garozzo, playing high-stake rubber bridge in Rome. At trick two he nonchalantly followed with the ♡K! Observe the effect: declarer, doubtless placing West with ♡ 9 x x x, returned to dummy's ♡J and then attempted to re-enter his hand with a club. Garozzo ruffed and cashed a winning diamond. To be sure, South has been guilty of greed or carelessness, but without Garozzo's virtuosity he would have had no problem.

Rubber bridge
North–South vulnerable
Dealer South

```
            ♠ K J 6 2
            ♡ A 8 4
            ◇ 9 5
            ♣ K J 5 2
♠ 10 5 4        ┌─────────┐
♡ K 10          │    N    │
◇ K Q J 8 6 3   │ W     E │
♣ 7 4           │    S    │
                └─────────┘
```

Bidding:

SOUTH	WEST	NORTH	EAST
1 ♠	2 ◇	4 ♠	Pass
5 ◇	Pass	5 ♡	Pass
6 ♠	Pass	Pass	Pass

West leads the king of diamonds against South's contract of six spades. East plays the seven and South wins with the ace. Three rounds of trumps follow, ending in declarer's hand. East has only one spade and discards the two of diamonds and the two of hearts. South now plays the three of hearts towards the dummy.

How should West plan the defence?

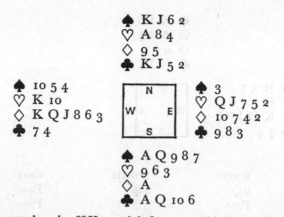

♠ K J 6 2
♡ A 8 4
◇ 9 5
♣ K J 5 2

♠ 10 5 4　　　　　　　　♠ 3
♡ K 10　　　　　　　　　♡ Q J 7 5 2
◇ K Q J 8 6 3　　　　　◇ 10 7 4 2
♣ 7 4　　　　　　　　　♣ 9 8 3

♠ A Q 9 8 7
♡ 9 6 3
◇ A
♣ A Q 10 6

West must play the ♡K at trick five to avoid the possibility of being endplayed and having to concede a ruff and discard. If he fails to do this declarer may complete a partial elimination, ruffing dummy's last diamond, cashing precisely two clubs and putting West on play with the ♡K.

When this hand occurred at the table West failed to play the ♡K at the first opportunity, but was given a second chance when South took *three* rounds of clubs, ending in dummy. Now West jettisoned the ♡K, leaving South with one more hope—that all the diamond honours were with West. Accordingly he led the ◇9, intending to discard a heart loser, but East was more alert than his partner and rose with the ◇10, leaving declarer with no further chance.

Rubber bridge
Game all
Dealer North

```
              ♠ A J 10
              ♡ Q 9 6
              ◇ 10 5 4
              ♣ A K J 7

                 ┌─────────┐
                 │    N    │     ♠ K 6 5
    ◇ 7 led      │ W     E │     ♡ A 3
                 │    S    │     ◇ K J 9 8 6 3
                 └─────────┘     ♣ 9 6
```

Bidding:

SOUTH	WEST	NORTH	EAST
		1 NT	2 ◇
3 ♠	Pass	4 ♠	Pass
Pass	Pass		

West leads the seven of diamonds against South's contract of four spades. East plays the eight and South the queen. The queen of clubs comes next and is followed by a low spade to the ace. On the ace of clubs South throws the two of hearts. He then plays dummy's king of clubs.

How should East plan the defence?

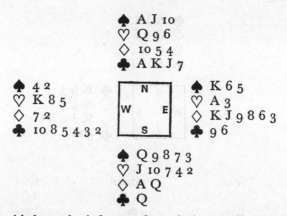

♠ A J 10
♡ Q 9 6
◇ 10 5 4
♣ A K J 7

♠ 4 2
♡ K 8 5
◇ 7 2
♣ 10 8 5 4 3 2

♠ K 6 5
♡ A 3
◇ K J 9 8 6 3
♣ 9 6

♠ Q 9 8 7 3
♡ J 10 7 4 2
◇ A Q
♣ Q

East should draw the inference from declarer's discard that he has ten cards in the major suits. Accordingly he should ruff the ♣K with the ♠K and play ♡A and another heart. The only real hope of beating the contract is to find West with the ♡K and pick up a ruff.

When this hand occurred East made the mistake of ruffing with the ♠6. South overruffed and played a spade, subsequently losing two heart tricks. Although it should not have affected the issue, South made the most of his chances by playing on clubs before giving up a trick to the ♠K.

Rubber bridge
North–South vulnerable
Dealer South

```
                        ♠ 8 6 4
                        ♡ A J 10 5
                        ◇ 7 5 3
                        ♣ 6 4 2

                    ┌─────────┐      ♠ 7 5 3
                    │    N    │      ♡ Q 4 3
          ♠Q led    │ W     E │      ◇ J 10
                    │    S    │      ♣ Q 10 9 5 3
                    └─────────┘
```

Bidding:

SOUTH	WEST	NORTH	EAST
2♣	Pass	2◇	Pass
2 NT	Pass	3 NT	Pass
Pass	Pass		

West leads the queen of spades against South's contract of three no
trumps. South wins the opening lead and plays the king of hearts
followed by the eight of hearts to dummy's ten—West follows with
the two and the seven.

How should East plan the defence?

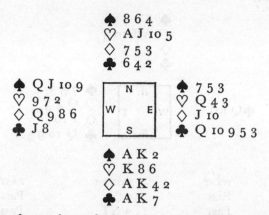

East's best chance is to duck without the slightest hesitation! If South can be tempted into repeating the finesse he may well finish up with a minus score.

When this hand occurred East did in fact duck without the suspicion of a trance. South greedily repeated the finesse and when the diamonds failed to break he suffered an ignominious defeat. On the following hand East–West bid and made game, and immediately after that they landed 6♠. 'The cards some people hold!' said South with feeling—if little justification.

Rubber bridge
Game all
Dealer West

```
                    ♠ 10 3
                    ♡ K Q 8
                    ◇ 8 5 3 2
                    ♣ K J 9 2
                              N        ♠ 9 7 6 4
   ♣3 led              W          E    ♡ 4 2
                              S        ◇ K 9
                                       ♣ A Q 8 6 5
```

Bidding:

SOUTH	WEST	NORTH	EAST
	3◇	Pass	Pass
4◇*	Pass	5◇	Pass
5♡	Pass	6♡	Pass
Pass	Pass		

* Showing a major two–suiter.

West leads the three of clubs against South's contract of six hearts.
Dummy plays the jack.
How should East plan the defence?

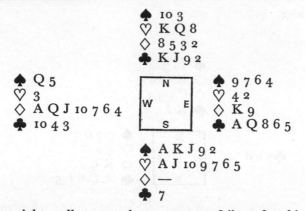

♠ 10 3
♡ K Q 8
◇ 8 5 3 2
♣ K J 9 2

♠ Q 5
♡ 3
◇ A Q J 10 7 6 4
♣ 10 4 3

♠ 9 7 6 4
♡ 4 2
◇ K 9
♣ A Q 8 6 5

♠ A K J 9 2
♡ A J 10 9 7 6 5
◇ —
♣ 7

East might well reason that success or failure for this hand will
depend not on the club suit but on the spade suit. If West has an
honour card in spades East must do all he can to persuade South to
take a losing finesse; thus the ♣A on the first round can hardly
cost. Put yourself in South's position. He ruffs the ◇K at trick two,
plays a heart to dummy and ruffs a club. He takes the ♠A, plays a
second heart to dummy, West showing out, and cashes ♣K. At
this point West is counted for one heart, one spade and—if he has
♣Q, which seems marked—four clubs. It is fair to assume a seven-
card diamond suit, as with ◇ K x x plus the ♣A East might well have
raised pre-emptively; alternatively, he might have led a low diamond, not the ◇K. Having counted thirteen cards in West's hand
without ♠Q it is difficult for South to avoid taking the obvious
finesse against East.

When this hand occurred at the table, Mrs Nan Klean, a most
imaginative and experienced rubber-bridge player, did in fact play
the ♣A at trick one, and she was subsequently rewarded when
declarer, counting with great care, tabled his cards and claimed his
contract by means of the marked spade finesse. When West produced
the ♠Q declarer's expression of astonishment would not have been
excelled by a child seeing Father Christmas without his beard.

Teams
Game all
Dealer South

```
                        ♠ K J 10 7 5
                        ♡ Q 8 3
                        ◇ Q 3 2
                        ♣ 7 3
                   ┌─────────┐      ♠ A Q 3
                   │    N    │      ♡ J 9 7 2
    ♣ J led        │ W     E │      ◇ A 8
                   │    S    │      ♣ A 6 4 2
                   └─────────┘
```

Bidding:

SOUTH	WEST	NORTH	EAST
1 ♡	Pass	1 ♠	Pass
2 NT	Pass	3 NT	Pass
Pass	Pass		

East has shown commendable restraint in the bidding, which is just as well since West is marked with almost a yarborough. However, West leads the jack of clubs against South's contract of three no trumps. East follows with the six and declarer wins with the queen. At trick two the king of diamonds falls to East's ace.

How should East plan the defence?

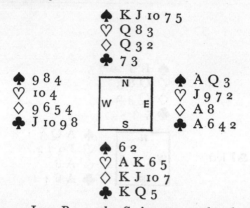

East, who was Jean Besse, the Swiss star, took a long time before playing to trick three. He appreciated that in the event of South's cashing his diamond winners he would have to find some awkward discards. One, ♠3, would be easy, but what about the second? If he fell for the temptation of playing off ♣A and another club at tricks three and four, then on the fourth diamond he would either have to part with his heart guard or lose the established club trick. Besse's elegant solution: return a low club at trick three, and then on the fourth diamond he would be able to spare his ♣A.

At the other table, defending against the same contract with the same opening lead, East did not see the dangers in time. At trick three he played ♣A and followed with a second club. Declarer won and cashed his diamond tricks plus three top hearts. This was the position with three cards left to play:

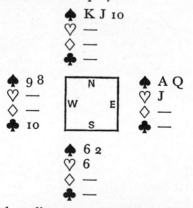

South was on lead needing one more trick for his contract, and East had to oblige when he was thrown in with the ♡J.

Teams
Love all
Dealer North

```
                    ♠ 6 3
                    ♡ A K Q 6
                    ◇ K 7
                    ♣ Q 9 8 5 4
                                        ♠ A 4
                         N              ♡ 8 2
    ♡J led          W         E         ◇ Q J 10 5 3
                         S              ♣ A K 3 2
```

Bidding:

SOUTH	WEST	NORTH	EAST
		1 ♣	Pass
1 ♠	Pass	1 NT	Pass
4 ♠	Pass	Pass	Pass

West leads the jack of hearts against South's contract of four spades. Declarer plays the three top hearts from dummy, discarding the six of clubs on the second round.

How should East conduct the defence?

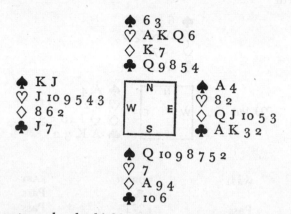

East has to make the highly imaginative play of ruffing with ♠A and continuing with ♠4. To justify this manœuvre he must visualize the power of his partner's trumps.

This hand occurred in the 1970 European Championship Trials for Estoril. The East hand was held by Terence Reese, who was quick to criticize himself when he ruffed with the ♠4. The contract was now made. It will be noticed that West must also play his part if the declarer is to be denied any chance of slipping home. Having taken the ♠ K J West must switch to a diamond to break up the minor-suit squeeze against East.

Of course declarer can always succeed if he plays three rounds of diamonds, ruffing the third round in dummy, before playing the third round of hearts . . . but then there would have been no problem.

Teams
East–West vulnerable
Dealer East

```
                        ♠ K 5
                        ♡ 9 4
                        ◇ Q J 10 7 5
                        ♣ Q J 9 6
        ♠ 8 6            ┌─────────┐
        ♡ 8 7 5          │    N    │
        ◇ 9 8 4 3 2      │ W     E │
        ♣ A 5 2          │    S    │
                        └─────────┘
```

Bidding:

SOUTH	WEST	NORTH	EAST
			1♣
2♣*	Pass	2◇	Pass
2♡	Pass	3 NT	Pass
4♡	Pass	Pass	Pass

* May be a two-suiter not very powerful in top cards.

West leads the seven of hearts against South's contract of four hearts. Dummy plays low, East the king and South the ace. South now sets about establishing the spades. The king and ace are followed by a small spade ruffed in dummy, on which West discards a low club, East contributing the jack of spades. The queen of diamonds is played from dummy, East winning with the ace. East cashes the queen of spades, South following with the nine.

How should West plan the defence?

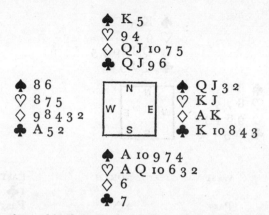

```
              ♠ K 5
              ♡ 9 4
              ♦ Q J 10 7 5
              ♣ Q J 9 6

♠ 8 6                          ♠ Q J 3 2
♡ 8 7 5            N           ♡ K J
♦ 9 8 4 3 2    W     E         ♦ A K
♣ A 5 2            S           ♣ K 10 8 4 3

              ♠ A 10 9 7 4
              ♡ A Q 10 6 3 2
              ♦ 6
              ♣ 7
```

West must throw his ♣A on the ♠Q, otherwise he will disrupt the timing for the trump-promotion play which is needed to defeat the contract. Once the ♣A is out of the way East will cash his ♣K and follow with a second club, promoting West's ♡8 to winning rank.

This hand occurred in a pre-European-Championship Trial Match between Holland and Great Britain played in Leiden, 1970. The declarer, South, was the 1966 World Pairs Champion, Hans Kreyns, and his partner was Jaap Kokkes. They were representing Holland in the open room. The British players were Jeremy Flint (East) and Jonathan Cansino (West). In fact the play went exactly as described, Jonathan Cansino discarding his ♣A as if it were an empty cigarette packet! As the cards lie declarer could have got home by drawing trumps and then playing East for both the missing spade honours, but surely cannot be criticized for the line he took.